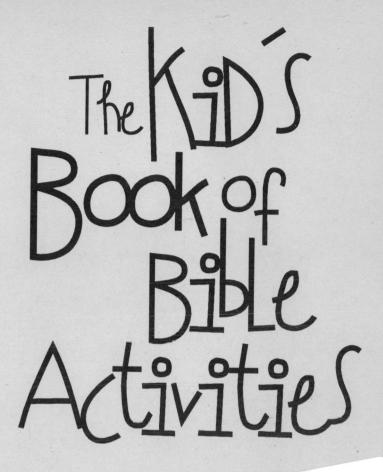

The Kid's Book of Bible Activities

Vicki Sav...

illustrated by Ke...

D0289566

BARBOUR
PUBLISHING, INC.
Uhrichsville, Ohio

© MCMXCVII by Barbour Publishing, Inc.

ISBN 1-57748-278-6

Published by Barbour Publishing, Inc.
P.O. Box 719
Uhrichsville, Ohio 44683
http://www.barbourbooks.com

 Member of the
Evangelical Christian
Publishers Association

Printed in the United States of America.

cover illustration by Ron Wheeler

TRAVEL THE PATH THAT MAKES A SENTENCE.

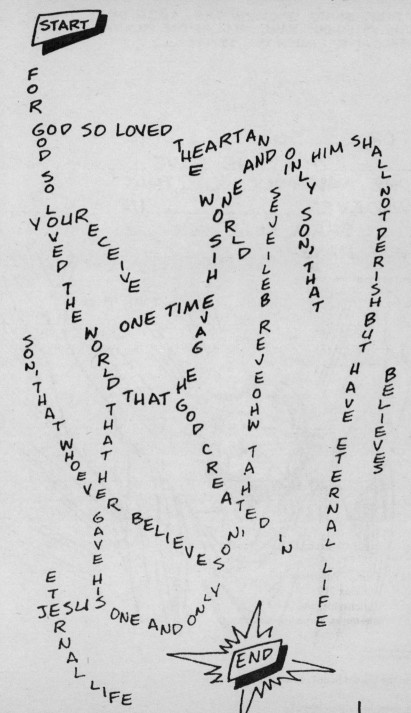

1

AFTER GOING THROUGH THE MAZE ON
THE PREVIOUS PAGE, FILL IN THE BLANKS
BELOW TO FINISH THE SENTENCE.

"FOR ___ SO _____ THE
_____ THAT HE GAVE ___
ONE AND ONLY ___, THAT
WHOEVER _____ IN
___ SHALL NOT _____
BUT HAVE _____
____."

JOHN 3:16

2

FIND THE WORDS BELOW IN THE
WORD SEARCH PUZZLE.

```
J R U A M D C I W A U I H X
M G O T P N S C S M L E I J
I O E B F T L O V E D Y M G
E D R K T B J F C V T G H K
Q L Q O S E H Q P B N I P L
E A D B E L I E V E S D M T
C H R X W B S C O G K O L Q
L W O R L D A S U D U F B W
W R Q G U H O A M V K L A J
I N B S D T Y N P W A I C Z
P K L Y V L O D U X Z F O S
Z P E R I S H B N V T E K V
H F I J G F Y X H C W B H F
P E T E R N A L T O B G Q J
D N R J G Z M E X Y N V R Z
```

ETERNAL   HIM

WORLD   LIFE

SON   BELIEVES

PERISH   HIS

GOD   LOVED

3

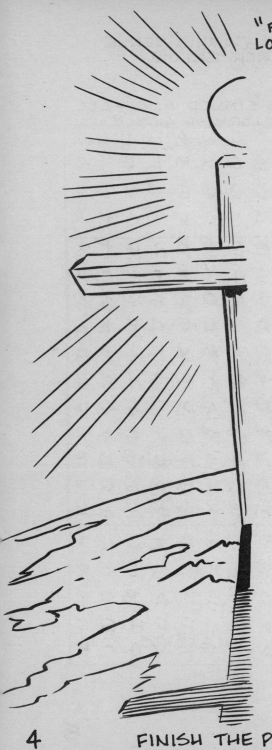

"FOR GOD SO LOVED THE WORLD..."

4   FINISH THE PICTURE.

FIND THE WORDS TO THIS VERSE IN THE WORDSEARCH BELOW.

"FOR ALL HAVE SINNED AND FALL SHORT OF THE GLORY OF GOD."

ROMANS 3:23

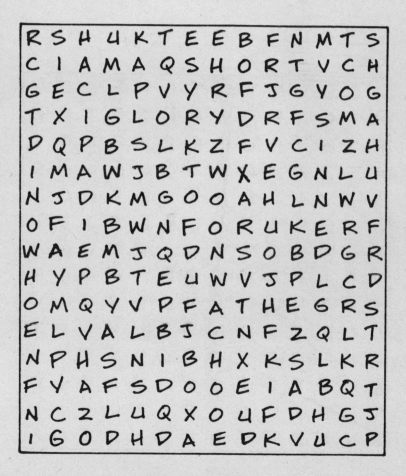

FIND THE WORDS TO THIS VERSE
IN THE WORDSEARCH BELOW.

"... WHILE WE WERE STILL SINNERS,
CHRIST DIED FOR US."

ROMANS 5:8b

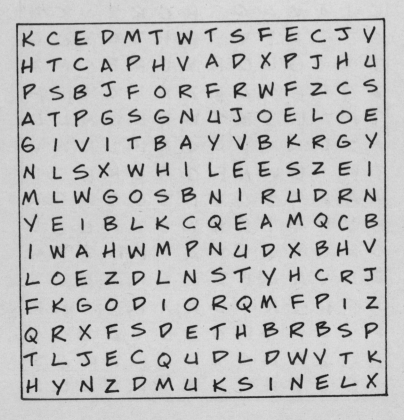

6

USE THE CODE CHART TO MATCH THE NUMBERS WITH LETTERS. USE THE COLUMN GOING DOWN, FIRST, THEN WRITE THE LETTERS IN THE BLANKS.

	1	2	3	4	5	6
1	A	F	K	P	U	Z
2	B	G	L	Q	V	
3	C	H	M	R	W	
4	D	I	N	S	X	
5	E	J	O	T	Y	

"
F O R   T H E   W A G E S O F
12 53 34   54 32 51   35 11 22 51 44 53 12

S I N   I S   D E A T H ' B U T
44 42 43   42 44   41 51 11 54 32 ' 21 15 54

T H E   G I F T   O F   G O D
54 32 51   22 42 12 54   53 12   22 53 41

I S   E T E R N A L   L I F E
42 44   51 54 51 34 43 11 23   23 42 12 51

I N   C H R I S T   J E S U S
42 43   31 32 34 42 44 54   52 51 44 15 44
"
O U R   L O R D .
53 15 34   23 53 34 41

ROMANS 6:23   7

CONNECT-THE-DOTS

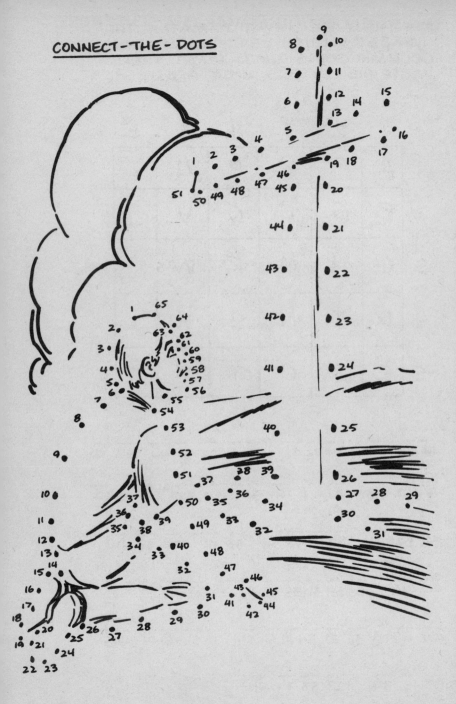

8

TRAVEL THE PATH THAT MAKES A SENTENCE.

START

I AM THE GOING TO THE CITY

THE WAY AND THE TRUTH AND

IN THE THOSE WHO K AND THE LIFE. NO ONE IS DISCIPLES COMES TO

HE A TRUTH N BUT A VAPOUR THE FATHER

BE R W O

G A NO ONE NO ONE CAN COME EXCEPT

I STILL COMESINNING BUT THE GRACE OF THROUGH

NO ONE COMES TO THE FATHER ME.

N

G GOD AND FATHER

YOU MUST BE BORN

END

9

JOHN 14:6

AFTER GOING THROUGH THE MAZE ON
THE PREVIOUS PAGE, FILL IN THE BLANKS
BELOW TO FINISH THE SENTENCE.

" I __ THE ____ AND THE
_____ AND THE ____.
NO ___ _____ TO
THE _____ EXCEPT
_____ __ . "

JOHN 14:6

NOW FIND THE UNDERLINED WORDS IN
THE WORDSEARCH BELOW.

USE THE CODE CHART TO MATCH THE
NUMBERS WITH LETTERS. USE THE
COLUMN GOING DOWN, FIRST, THEN
WRITE THE LETTERS IN THE BLANKS.

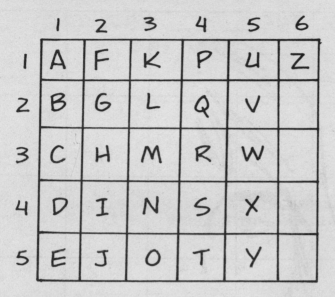

	1	2	3	4	5	6
1	A	F	K	P	U	Z
2	B	G	L	Q	V	
3	C	H	M	R	W	
4	D	I	N	S	X	
5	E	J	O	T	Y	

JOHN 5:24a

"

42 54 51 23 23   55 53 15   54 32 51

54 34 15 54 32 ' 35 32 53 51 25 51 34

32 51 11 34 44   33 55   35 53 34 41

11 43 41 21 51 23 42 51 25 51 44

32 42 33 35 32 53 44 51 43 54 33 51

32 11 44 51 54 51 34 43 11 23

23 42 12 51 11 43 41 35 42 23 23 43 53 54 "

21 51 31 53 43 41 51 33 43 51 41 ...

"

FINISH THE PICTURE OF JESUS.

TRAVEL THE PATH THAT MAKES A SENTENCE.

START

END

13

ROMANS 10:9

AFTER GOING THROUGH THE MAZE ON
THE PREVIOUS PAGE, FILL IN THE BLANKS
BELOW TO FINISH THE SENTENCE.

"IF YOU _ _ _ _ _ _ _
WITH YOUR _ _ _ _ _ _,
' _ _ _ _ _ _ IS _ _ _ _', AND
_ _ _ _ _ _ _ _ IN YOUR
_ _ _ _ _ _ THAT GOD
_ _ _ _ _ _ HIM FROM
THE _ _ _ _, YOU WILL BE
_ _ _ _ _ ."

ROMANS 10:9

14

FIND THE WORDS BELOW IN THE WORDSEARCH PUZZLE.

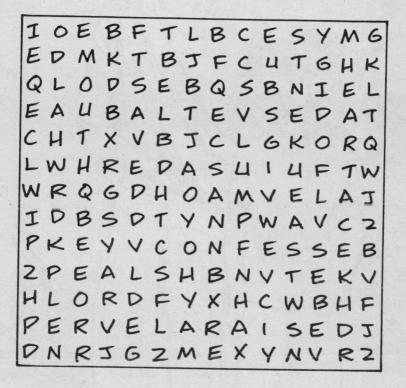

```
I O E B F T L B C E S Y M G
E D M K T B J F C U T G H K
Q L O D S E B Q S B N I E L
E A U B A L T E V S E D A T
C H T X V B J C L G K O R Q
L W H R E D A U I U F T W
W R Q G D H O A M V E L A J
I D B S D T Y N P W A V C Z
P K E Y V C O N F E S S E B
Z P E A L S H B N V T E K V
H L O R D F Y X H C W B H F
P E R V E L A R A I S E D J
D N R J G Z M E X Y N V R Z
```

LORD   RAISED

HEART   MOUTH

DEAD   BELIEVE

CONFESS   JESUS

SAVED   15

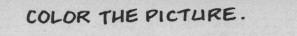

COLOR THE PICTURE.

JESUS IS KNOCKING AT THE DOOR OF YOUR HEART. WHAT SHOULD YOU DO?

USE THE CODE CHART BELOW TO MATCH THE CODES WITH LETTERS. USE THE COLUMN GOING DOWN FIRST. THEN WRITE THE LETTERS IN THE BLANKS TO COMPLETE THE VERSE.

THEN YOU WILL KNOW WHAT TO DO!

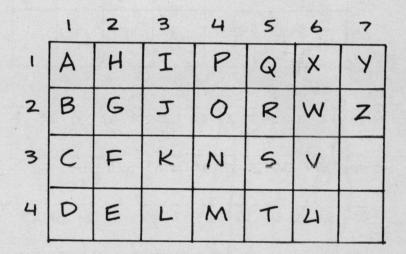

"
‾‾ ‾‾ ‾‾ ‾‾ ‾‾ ‾‾ ‾‾ ! ‾‾ ‾‾ ‾‾ ‾‾ ‾‾ ‾‾
12 42 25 42 13 11 44   13 35 45 11 34 41

‾‾ ‾‾ ‾‾ ‾‾ ‾‾ ‾‾ ‾‾ ‾‾ ‾‾ ‾‾ ‾‾ ‾‾
11 45 45 12 42 41 24 24 25 11 34 41

‾‾ ‾‾ ‾‾ ‾‾ ‾‾ "
33 34 24 31 33

CONTINUED NEXT PAGE...

17

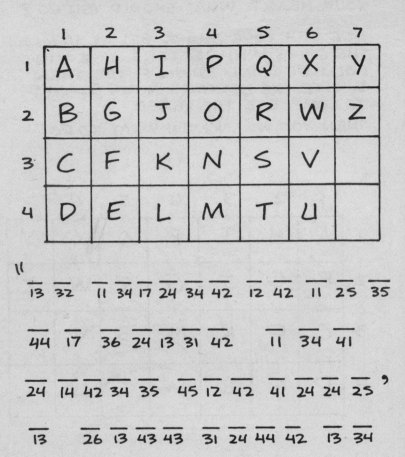

19

DO YOU KNOW JESUS LOVES YOU? DO YOU KNOW HOW MUCH JESUS LOVES YOU? HE LOVES YOU SO MUCH THAT HE DIED TO PAY THE PRICE FOR YOUR SIN. THERE IS ONLY ONE SIN THAT GOD WILL NOT FORGIVE. THAT SIN IS NOT BELIEVING IN JESUS AND WHAT HE DID FOR YOU AND ALL OF US. WITHOUT JESUS, WITHOUT ACCEPTING THAT HE DIED FOR US, NO ONE CAN GO TO HEAVEN.

THREE DAYS AFTER JESUS DIED, HE WAS RAISED TO NEW LIFE. HE WANTS TO SHARE THAT WITH US TOO! HE WANTS TO GIVE US NEW LIFE ... ETERNAL LIFE!

DO YOU WANT TO ASK JESUS TO COME INTO YOUR HEART AND YOUR LIFE? ALL YOU NEED TO DO IS ASK HIM. YOU COULD SAY A PRAYER LIKE THIS:

> DEAR JESUS,
>
> I KNOW I AM A SINNER AND THAT YOU DIED FOR ALL MY SINS. I KNOW YOU ROSE FROM THE DEAD. JESUS, I ASK YOU NOW TO COME INTO MY HEART AND TAKE CONTROL OF MY LIFE.
> THANK YOU FOR ALL YOU HAVE DONE FOR ME.
> TEACH ME YOUR WAYS, JESUS, AND HELP ME TO GROW UP WITH YOU.
>
> IN JESUS' NAME, I PRAY. AMEN.

IF YOU HAVE NEVER INVITED JESUS INTO YOUR HEART AND LIFE BUT YOU WANT TO NOW, GO TO THE NEXT PAGE AND WRITE OUT YOUR PRAYER IN YOUR OWN WORDS. JUST TELL JESUS HOW YOU REALLY FEEL.

MY VERY OWN PRAYER TO INVITE
JESUS INTO MY HEART AND LIFE.

DATE : _____

DEAR LORD JESUS,

_____

_____

_____

_____

_____

_____

_____

_____

_____

_____

                    IN JESUS' NAME, AMEN.

                    _____
                         YOUR NAME

DID YOU INVITE JESUS INTO YOUR HEART?

FIND YOUR WAY TO JESUS :

WOW! IF YOU ASKED JESUS INTO YOUR LIFE, YOU ARE NOW A CHRISTIAN! YOU ARE NOW A CHILD OF GOD!

LET'S LEARN HOW TO GET TO KNOW JESUS BETTER.

UNSCRAMBLE THE WORDS BELOW TO FIND OUT HOW TO BEGIN.

1.) TO BECOME A CHILD OF GOD, YOU HAD TO ASK JESUS INTO YOUR HEART. THIS IS CALLED _____ .
IYGNRAP

2.) PRAYING IS _____ WITH GOD.
GTINALK

3.) JUST LIKE YOU TALK WITH YOUR MOM OR DAD, GOD_____ YOU TO _____ WITH HIM.   TWNAS   KTLA

4.) IT DOES NOT STOP THERE. GOD WANTS TO TALK TO YOU! JESUS SPEAKS TO YOU THROUGH HIS _____ .
DRWO

5.) THE ONLY WAY TO REALLY KNOW JESUS IS TO_____ ABOUT_____ .
ARDE   IMH

6.) YOU READ ABOUT _____ IN THE HOLY
_____ .   JSSUE
EBLIB

IN THE FOLLOWING WORDSEARCH PUZZLE,
FIND AND CIRCLE THE WORDS LISTED.

THEY CAN BE FOUND IN LINES GOING
FORWARD, BACKWARD, UP, DOWN, OR
DIAGONALLY.

```
D F C L P V Y R F H G V O G
O X S R A E H Y D R I S M A
O Q P B S L K Z F V C M Z H
R M B W J B E A T H G N L V
N J D K M N Q O A H L N W O
O F I B O N F O D U K R P I
W A E Y J Q D N S N B D G C
H K N O C K U W V J A L C E
O A Q Y V P F A T P B T R S
V L E A L B D E V O L Q S T
```

LOVED	HEARS	EAT
KNOCK	VOICE	ANYONE
DOOR	HIM	STAND

24

WHAT HAVE YOU LEARNED ABOUT BEING A CHILD OF GOD?

FIND AND CIRCLE THE WORDS LISTED BELOW.

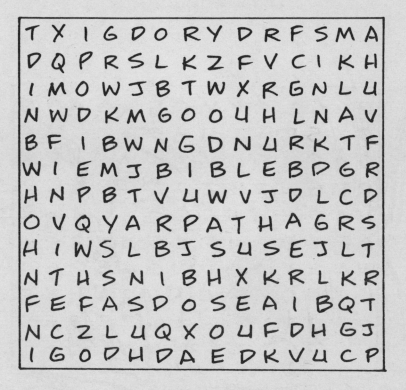

```
T X I G D O R Y D R F S M A
D Q P R S L K Z F V C I K H
I M O W J B T W X R G N L U
N W D K M G O O U H L N A V
B F I B W N G D N U R K T F
W I E M J B I B L E B D G R
H N P B T V U W V J D L C D
O V Q Y A R P A T H A G R S
H I W S L B J S U S E J L T
N T H S N I B H X K R L K R
F E F A S D O S E A I B Q T
N C Z L U Q X O U F D H G J
I G O D H D A E D K V U C P
```

PRAY   WORD   TALK

READ   JESUS   GOD

BIBLE   SAVIOUR   INVITE

25

CONNECT THE DOTS
AND FINISH THE PHRASE.

JESUS, THE _ _ _ _ _ OF JUDAH!

26

ACROSS

1. GOD <u>EAVG</u> US HIS ONE AND ONLY SON.

2. NOW WE CAN HAVE ETERNAL <u>FILE</u>.

3. JESUS KNOCKS AT THE DOORS OF OUR <u>TARHES</u>

4. IF WE HAVE <u>TIVDEIN</u> HIM IN, HE WILL NEVER <u>LEAVE US</u>.

DOWN

5. WE ARE NOW A CHILD OF <u>ODG</u>.

6. WE TALK TO HIM BY <u>YRANIGP</u>.

7. HE TALKS TO US THROUGH <u>SHI</u> WORD.

8. HIS WORD IS THE <u>BBEIL</u>.

<u>WORD LIST</u>

PRAYING	HEARTS
LIFE	BIBLE
GAVE	HIS
INVITED	GOD

27

28

SOMETIMES, IT'S NOT EASY TO READ THE BIBLE EVERY DAY. OTHER *THINGS* WILL TRY TO GET IN THE WAY, BUT IF YOU REALLY WANT TO GROW AS A CHRISTIAN, IT IS BEST TO READ IN GOD'S WORD EACH DAY.

FIND YOUR WAY TO THE BIBLE.

START

↓ NOW ↓ WHEN THE COUNSELOR

↓ MAKING I AM PLAINLY ABOUT MY

IT GOING HAVE CHOSEN

KNOWN TO BUT WILL I WHOM, COMES

I AM COMING SEND TO YOU TO THIS ETERNAL LIFE

I HAVE FROM EACH

SPIRIT THE , FATHER THE IS ETERNAL LIFE TO HIS

OLD YOU TRUTH

OF TRUTH WHO GOES OUT THE SPIRIT OF FROM THE

THESE

TESTIFY WILL HE LIGHTS OF , FATHER

WILL SEE ABOUT ME. NO FOR

END

30

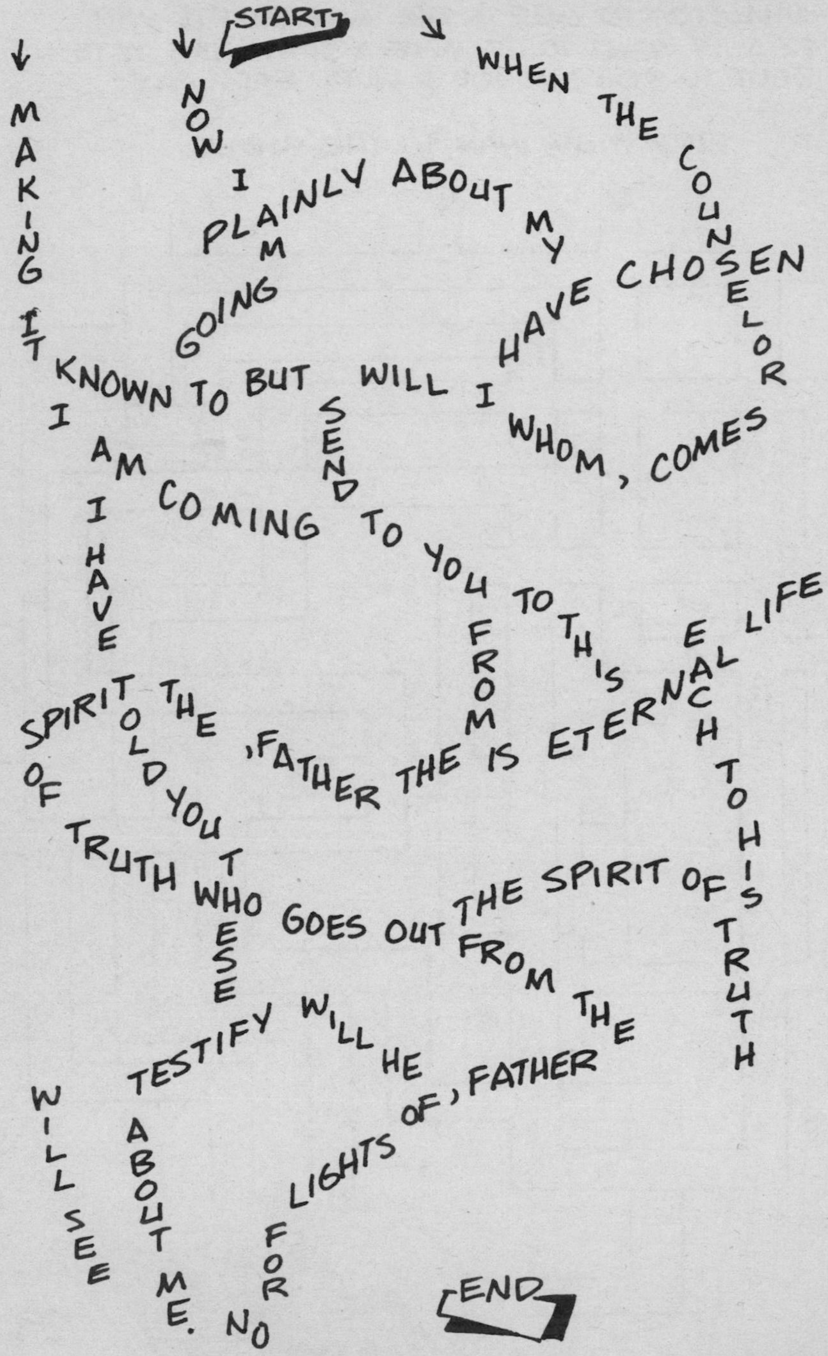

JOHN 15:26

AFTER GOING THROUGH THE MAZE ON
THE PREVIOUS PAGE, FILL IN THE BLANKS
BELOW TO FINISH THE SENTENCE.

"WHEN THE ___ ___ ___ ___ ___ ___ ___ ___ ___ ___ ___
COMES, ___ ___ ___ ___ I WILL
___ ___ ___ ___ TO ___ ___ ___ FROM THE
___ ___ ___ ___ ___ ___ , THE ___ ___ ___ ___ ___ ___
OF ___ ___ ___ ___ ___ WHO ___ ___ ___ ___
OUT FROM THE FATHER, HE
WILL ___ ___ ___ ___ ___ ___ ___
___ ___ ___ ___ ___ ME."

JOHN 15:26

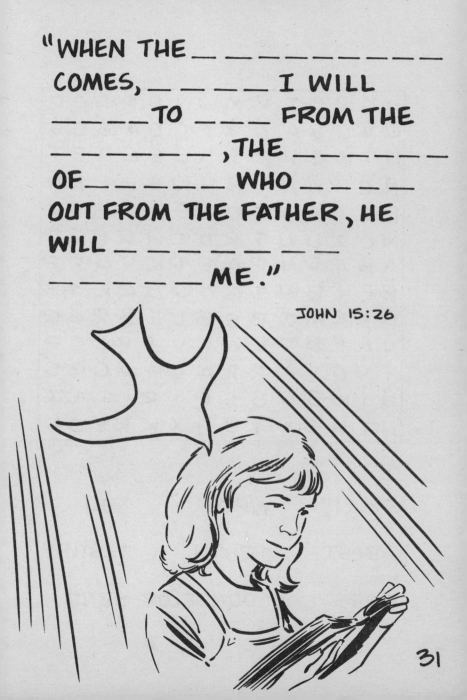

FIND THE WORDS BELOW IN THE WORDSEARCH PUZZLE.

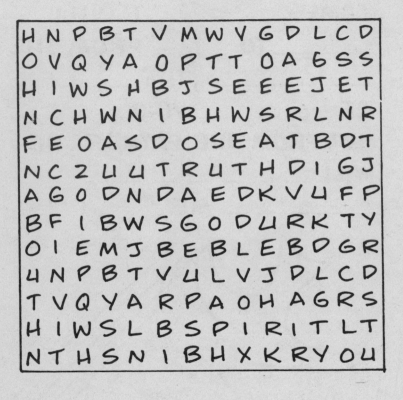

```
H N P B T V M W V G D L C D
O V Q Y A O P T T O A G S S
H I W S H B J S E E E J E T
N C H W N I B H W S R L N R
F E O A S D O S E A T B D T
N C Z U U T R U T H D I G J
A G O D N D A E D K V U F P
B F I B W S G O D U R K T Y
O I E M J B E B L E B D G R
U N P B T V U L V J D L C D
T V Q Y A R P A O H A G R S
H I W S L B S P I R I T L T
N T H S N I B H X K R Y O U
```

SPIRIT   WHOM   YOU

ABOUT   TRUTH   TESTIFY

GOES   COUNSELOR   SEND

COLOR THE PICTURE

WHEN YOU BECOME A CHILD OF GOD, WHERE DOES THE HOLY SPIRIT LIVE?

GO ON TO THE NEXT PAGE TO FIND THE ANSWER.

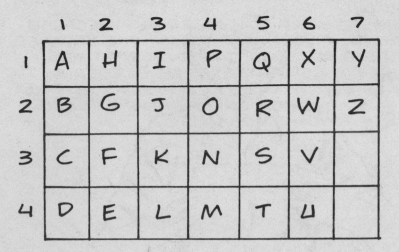

	1	2	3	4	5	6	7
1	A	H	I	P	Q	X	Y
2	B	G	J	O	R	W	Z
3	C	F	K	N	S	V	
4	D	E	L	M	T	U	

"

___ ___ ___ ___ ___   ___ ___ ___   ___ ___ ___ ___
41 24 17 24 46   34 24 45   33 34 24 26

___ ___ ___ ___   ___ ___ ___ ___   ___ ___ ___ ___
45 12 11 45   17 24 46 25   21 24 41 17

___ ___   ___   ___ ___ ___ ___ ___ ___   ___ ___
13 35   11   45 42 44 14 43 42   24 32

___ ___ ___   ___ ___ ___ ___   ___ ___ ___ ___ ___ ___ ___'
45 12 42   12 24 43 17   35 14 13 25 13 45'

___ ___ ___   ___ ___ ___ ___   ___ ___ ___'
26 12 24   13 35 13 34   17 24 46'

___ ___ ___ ___   ___ ___ ___   ___ ___ ___ ___
26 12 24 44   17 24 46   12 11 36 42

?"
___ ___ ___ ___ ___ ___ ___ ___   ___ ___ ___ ___   ___ ___ ___
25 42 31 42 13 36 42 41   32 25 24 44   22 24 41

34

1 CORINTHIANS 6:19

THE HOLY SPIRIT ACTUALLY COMES TO
LIVE INSIDE YOU! YOUR BODY BECOMES
THE TEMPLE, OR DWELLING PLACE, OF GOD'S
SPIRIT.

THIS IS HARD TO UNDERSTAND BECAUSE
WE CAN'T SEE HIM, BUT IT IS TRUE BECAUSE
THE BIBLE SAYS IT IS SO. MANY TIMES
THE HOLY SPIRIT MAKES HIS PRESENCE
KNOWN. WE CAN FEEL HIM AS HE GIVES
US HIS POWER AND STRENGTH TO LIVE
AS GOD WANTS US TO LIVE.

CONNECT-THE-DOTS

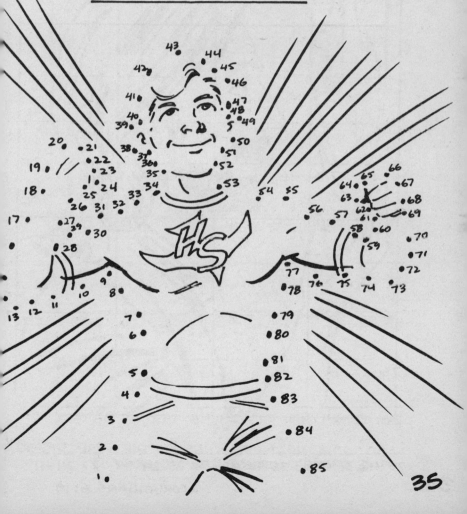

ONCE, OUR HUMAN SPIRITS WERE DEAD. WE WERE BORN SPIRITUALLY DEAD. JESUS GIVES US NEW LIFE IN OUR SPIRITS!

"FOR JUST AS THE FATHER RAISES THE DEAD AND GIVES THEM LIFE, EVEN SO THE SON GIVES LIFE TO WHOM HE IS PLEASED TO GIVE IT."

JOHN 5:21

GO TO THE NEXT PAGE. USING THE GRID, DRAW THE ABOVE PICTURE FOR YOURSELF.

FROM THE PREVIOUS PAGE, USE THE
GRID TO DRAW THE PICTURE FOR YOURSELF.

NOW THAT YOU ARE A CHRISTIAN, YOU MUST LET THE HOLY SPIRIT TEACH YOU HOW TO LIVE YOUR NEW LIFE. HOW DOES HE DO THIS?

USE THE CODE CHART BELOW TO MATCH THE CODES WITH LETTERS. USE THE COLUMN GOING DOWN, FIRST, THEN WRITE THE LETTERS IN THE BLANKS ON THE FOLLOWING PAGE.

	1	2	3	4	5	6	7
1	A	B	C	D	E	F	G
2	H	I	J	K	L	M	N
3	O	P	Q	R	S	T	U
4	V	W	X	Y	Z		

WHAT YOU PUT INTO YOUR MIND, WHAT YOU READ OR WATCH OR LISTEN TO, IS WHAT WILL COME OUT OF YOU. IF YOU PUT GOD'S WORD IN, IF YOU READ THE BIBLE REGULARLY, GOD'S CHARACTER WILL COME OUT OF YOU IN THE WAYS YOU THINK, ACT AND THE CHOICES YOU MAKE.

USING THE CODE CHART FROM THE
PREVIOUS PAGE, COMPLETE THE VERSE
BELOW.

(1

__ __   __ __ __   __ __ __ __ __ __ __
14 31 27 31 36 13 31 27 16 31 34 26

__ __ __   __ __ __ __ __ __   __ __ __ __ __ __
11 27 44 25 31 27 17 15 34 36 31 36 21 15

__ __ __ __ __ __ __   __ __   __ __ __ __
32 11 36 36 15 34 27 31 16 36 21 22 35

__ __ __ __ __ ,   __ __ __   __ __
42 31 34 25 14   12 37 36   12 15

__ __ __ __ __ __ __ __ __ __ __   __ __
36 34 11 27 35 16 31 34 26 15 14   12 44

__ __ __   __ __ __ __ __ __ __ __ __
36 21 15 34 15 27 15 42 22 27 17

                                            ))
__ __   __ __ __ __   __ __ __ __ .
31 16 44 31 37 34 26 22 27 14

ROMANS 12:2

COLOR THE PICTURE

BE CAREFUL IN YOUR CHOICES!

40

TRAVEL THE PATH THAT MAKES A SENTENCE.

START

DO NOT

ANYONE WHO RECEIVES THE SPIRIT USE LOVE JOY PEACE

BUT THE FRUIT OF

YOUR

LET US

FULNESS GOODNESS KINDNESS PATIENCE NOT

FAITH THOSE WHO WANT TO MAKE A COME BE

GENTLENESS BROTHER

GROW WEARY AND THE PEACE

WERE AND MERCY TO ALL WHO NOT BECOME

LET US

SELF-CONTROL.

CALLED TO BE

END

41

GALATIANS 5: 22-23a

AFTER GOING THROUGH THE MAZE ON THE PREVIOUS PAGE, FILL IN THE BLANKS BELOW TO FINISH THE VERSE.

"BUT THE _ _ _ _ _ _ OF

THE _ _ _ _ _ _ _ IS

_ _ _ _ _ , _ _ _ _ ,

_ _ _ _ _ _ _ ,

_ _ _ _ _ _ _ _ _ _ _ ,

_ _ _ _ _ _ _ _ _ _ _ ,

_ _ _ _ _ _ _ _ _ _ _ ,

_ _ _ _ _ _ _ _ _ _ _ _ ,

_ _ _ _ _ _ _ _ _ _ _ _ _

AND _ _ _ _ _ - _ _ _ _ _ _ _ ."

GALATIANS 5:22-23 a

FIND THE WORDS BELOW IN THE WORDSEARCH PUZZLE.

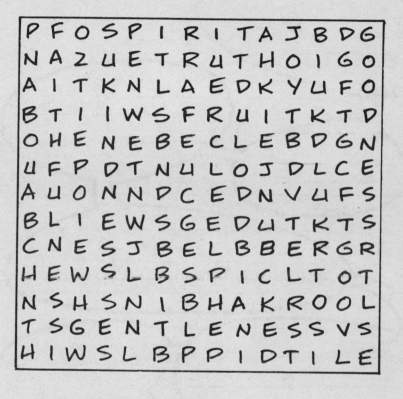

```
P F O S P I R I T A J B D G
N A Z U E T R U T H O I G O
A I T K N L A E D K Y U F O
B T I I W S F R U I T K T D
O H E N E B E C L E B D G N
U F P D T N U L O J D L C E
A U O N N D C E D N U F S
B L I E W S G E D U T K T S
C N E S J B E L B B E R G R
H E W S L B S P I C L T O T
N S H S N I B H A K R O O L
T S G E N T L E N E S S V S
H I W S L B P P I D T I L E
```

JOY

SELF-CONTROL

GENTLENESS

PEACE

FRUIT

FAITHFULNESS

KINDNESS

SPIRIT

PATIENCE

GOODNESS

LOVE

43

THE FRUIT OF THE SPIRIT

FILL IN THE BLANKS.

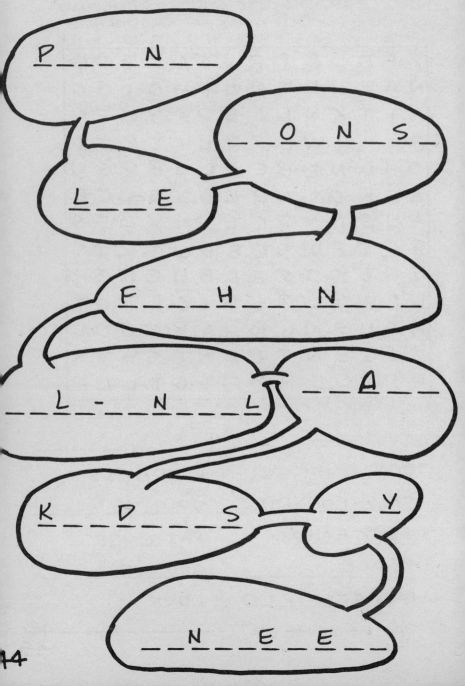

YOU ALREADY KNOW THAT WHEN YOU BECOME A CHRISTIAN, THE HOLY SPIRIT COMES TO LIVE IN YOU. THE HOLY SPIRIT WILL LEAD YOU INTO GOD'S TRUTH, AND HE WILL DO THE WORK OF PRODUCING GOD'S CHARACTER IN YOU, IF YOU WILL LET HIM. YOU CAN DO THAT BY CHOOSING TO DO WHAT GOD WANTS RATHER THAN WHAT YOU WANT. THIS IS CALLED SURRENDERING, OR GIVING UP, TO GOD'S WILL.

GOD'S CHARACTER IS THE FRUIT OF THE SPIRIT.

UNSCRAMBLE THE WORDS BELOW TO FIND GOD'S CHARACTER, THE FRUIT OF THE SPIRIT.

OVLE   _ _ _ _

OYJ   _ _ _

PCEEA   _ _ _ _ _

TIEENCPA _ _ _ _ _ _ _ _

DNNESKSI _ _ _ _ _ _ _ _

OGDOSSNE _ _ _ _ _ _ _ _

HTAIFLUNFSES

_ _ _ _ _ _ _ _ _ _ _ _

TNLEEEGSSN

_ _ _ _ _ _ _ _ _ _

- RTNSFLEOCLO

_ _ _ _ _ - _ _ _ _ _ _ _

45

FIND YOUR WAY THROUGH THE OBSTACLES, THE THINGS OF THIS WORLD, THAT WILL TRY TO PULL YOU AWAY FROM WHAT GOD WOULD WANT YOU TO DO.

END

FINISH THE PICTURE

AS YOU START TO LIVE YOUR NEW LIFE AS GOD'S CHILD, IT IS IMPORTANT TO KNOW WHO YOUR ENEMIES ARE!

THE CHRISTIAN HAS THREE ENEMIES:
1. THE DEVIL
2. THE SINFUL NATURE (THE FLESH)
3. THE WORLD

A CHRISTIAN IN THIS WORLD IS LIKE A SOLDIER — A SOLDIER OF THE LORD. YOUR ONLY WEAPON IS THE BIBLE.

47

USE THE CODE CHART BELOW TO MATCH
THE CODES WITH LETTERS. USE THE
COLUMN GOING DOWN, FIRST, THEN
WRITE THE LETTERS IN THE BLANKS.

	1	2	3	4	5	6	7
1	A	B	C	D	E	F	G
2	H	I	J	K	L	M	N
3	O	P	Q	R	S	T	U
4	V	W	X	Y	Z		

"

___ ___   ___ ___ ___ ___   ___ ___ ___ ___ ___ ___ ___ ___ ___
12 15   35 15 25 16   13 31 27 36 34 31 25 25 15

___ ___ ___   ___ ___ ___ ___ ___ .   ___ ___ ___ ___
11 27 14   11 25 15 34 36   44 31 37 34

___ ___ ___ ___ ___   ___ ___ ___   ___ ___ ___ ___ ___
15 27 15 26 44   36 21 15   14 15 41 22 25

___ ___ ___ ___ ___ ___   ___ ___ ___ ___ ___ ___
32 34 31 42 25 35   11 34 31 37 27 14

___ ___ ___ ___   ___   ___ ___ ___ ___ ___ ___ ___
25 22 24 15   11   34 31 11 34 22 27 17

___ ___ ___ ___   ___ ___ ___ ___ ___ ___ ___
25 22 31 27   25 31 31 24 22 27 17

___ ___ ___   ___ ___ ___ ___ ___ ___ ___
16 31 34   35 31 26 18 31 27 15

                                    "
___ ___   ___ ___ ___ ___ ___ ___ .
36 31   14 15 41 31 37 34

1 PETER 5:8

OUR LORD NEVER LEAVES HIS CHILDREN
HELPLESS. HE ALWAYS GIVES US A WAY
TO STAND AGAINST OUR ENEMY THE
DEVIL.
TO FIND OUT HOW, USE THE CODE CHART BELOW
TO COMPLETE THE VERSE. USE THE COLUMN
GOING DOWN FIRST.

	1	2	3	4	5	6	7
1	A	B	C	D	E	F	G
2	H	I	J	K	L	M	N
3	O	P	Q	R	S	T	U
4	V	W	X	Y	Z		

$\overline{35}\ \overline{37}\ \overline{12}\ \overline{26}\ \overline{22}\ \overline{36}\quad \overline{44}\ \overline{31}\ \overline{37}\ \overline{34}\ \overline{}$

$\overline{35}\ \overline{15}\ \overline{25}\ \overline{41}\ \overline{15}\ \overline{35}{}^{'}\ \overline{36}\ \overline{21}\ \overline{15}\ \overline{27}{}^{,}\ \overline{36}\ \overline{31}$

$\overline{17}\ \overline{31}\ \overline{14}\ .\ \overline{34}\ \overline{15}\ \overline{35}\ \overline{22}\ \overline{35}\ \overline{36}$

$\overline{36}\ \overline{21}\ \overline{15}\quad \overline{14}\ \overline{15}\ \overline{41}\ \overline{22}\ \overline{25}{}^{,}$

$\overline{11}\ \overline{27}\ \overline{14}\quad \overline{21}\ \overline{15}\quad \overline{42}\ \overline{22}\ \overline{25}\ \overline{25}$

$\overline{16}\ \overline{25}\ \overline{15}\ \overline{15}\quad \overline{16}\ \overline{34}\ \overline{31}\ \overline{26}\quad \overline{44}\ \overline{31}\ \overline{37}{}^{))}\ .$

JAMES 4:7

49

CONNECT-THE-DOTS

"... RESIST THE DEVIL, AND HE WILL FLEE..."

WHAT DO YOU NEED TO DO WHEN THE
DEVIL TEMPTS YOU TO SIN?

AS YOU GO THROUGH THE MAZE, COLLECT
THE LETTERS AND COMPLETE THE
STATEMENT BELOW.

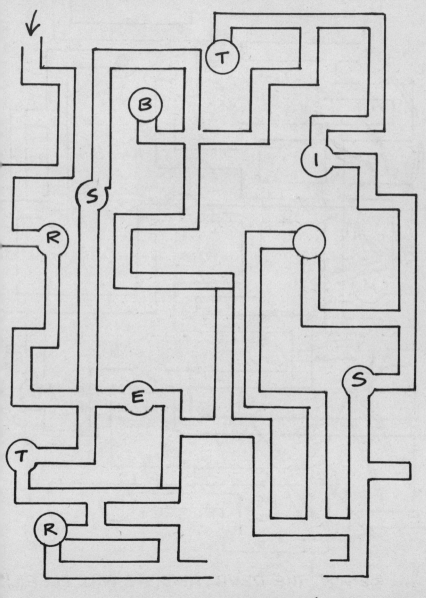

_ _ _ _ _ _ _ THE DEVIL !   51

WHAT IS THE DEVIL LIKE ?

AS YOU GO THROUGH THE MAZE, COLLECT THE LETTERS AND COMPLETE THE STATEMENT BELOW.

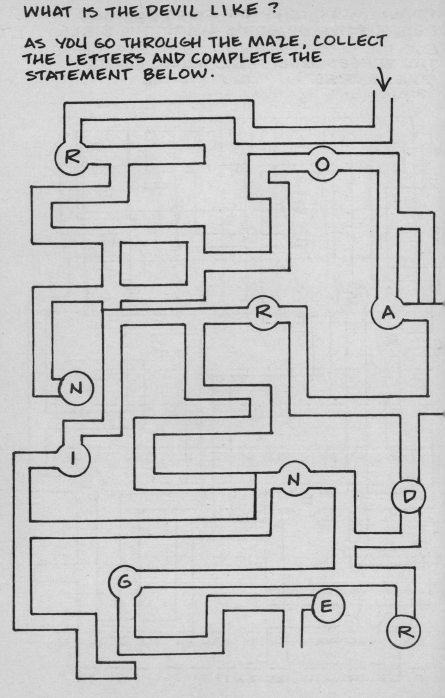

52 THE DEVIL IS LIKE A _ _ _ _ _ _ LION

PSALM 119: 104-105 GIVES ANOTHER DESCRIPTION OF GOD'S WORD, THE BIBLE. USE THE CODE BELOW TO COMPLETE THESE TWO VERSES. USE THE COLUMN GOING DOWN FIRST.

	1	2	3	4	5	6	7
1	A	B	C	D	E	F	G
2	H	I	J	K	L	M	N
3	O	P	Q	R	S	T	U
4	V	W	X	Y	Z		

(

22 17 11 22 27   37 27 14 15 34 ‾

35 36 11 27 14 22 27 17   16 34 31 26

44 31 37 34   32 34 15 13 15 32 36 35 ;

36 21 15 34 15 16 31 34 15   22

21 11 36 15   15 41 15 34 44

42 34 31 27 17 32 11 36 21 .

44 31 37 34   42 31 34 14   22 35   11

25 11 26 32   36 31   26 44 16 15 15 36

11 27 14   11   25 22 17 21 36   16 31 34
                              11

26 44   32 11 36 21 .

53

THE BIBLE IS A LAMP THAT LIGHTS OUR
WAY IN THE DARKNESS OF SIN AND
TEMPTATION.

USING THE GRID, DRAW THE PICTURE
BELOW ON THE NEXT PAGE.

FROM THE PREVIOUS PAGE, USE THE
GRID TO DRAW THE PICTURE FOR YOURSELF.

THE SECOND ENEMY IN OUR WALK WITH THE LORD IS OUR SINFUL NATURE, ALSO KNOWN AS THE "FLESH". THIS SINFUL NATURE OR FLESH IS A PART OF ALL OF US. WE ARE BORN WITH IT.

USE THE CODE CHART BELOW TO MATCH THE CODES WITH LETTERS. USE THE COLUMN GOING DOWN, FIRST, THEN WRITE THE LETTERS IN THE BLANKS.

	1	2	3	4	5	6	7
4			Z	Y	X	W	V
3	O	P	Q	R	S	T	U
2	N	M	L	K	J	I	H
1	A	B	C	D	E	F	G

((

$\overline{36}\ \overline{27}\ \overline{15}$ $\overline{11}\ \overline{13}\ \overline{36}\ \overline{35}$ $\overline{31}\ \overline{16}$ $\overline{36}\ \overline{27}\ \overline{15}$

$\overline{35}\ \overline{26}\ \overline{21}\ \overline{16}\ \overline{37}\ \overline{23}$ $\overline{21}\ \overline{11}\ \overline{36}\ \overline{37}\ \overline{34}\ \overline{15}$ $\overline{11}\ \overline{34}\ \overline{15}$

$\overline{11}\ \overline{21}\ \overline{17}\ \overline{15}\ \overline{34}$, $\overline{25}\ \overline{15}\ \overline{11}\ \overline{23}\ \overline{31}\ \overline{37}\ \overline{35}\ \overline{44}$,

$\overline{21}\ \overline{31}\ \overline{36}$ $\overline{35}\ \overline{27}\ \overline{11}\ \overline{34}\ \overline{26}\ \overline{21}\ \overline{17}$, $\overline{27}\ \overline{11}\ \overline{36}\ \overline{26}\ \overline{21}\ \overline{17}$,

$\overline{23}\ \overline{44}\ \overline{26}\ \overline{21}\ \overline{17}$, $\overline{22}\ \overline{11}\ \overline{24}\ \overline{26}\ \overline{21}\ \overline{17}$ $\overline{31}\ \overline{36}\ \overline{27}\ \overline{15}\ \overline{34}\ \overline{35}$

$\overline{11}\ \overline{21}\ \overline{17}\ \overline{34}\ \overline{44}$, $\overline{46}\ \overline{31}\ \overline{34}\ \overline{35}\ \overline{27}\ \overline{26}\ \overline{32}\ \overline{26}\ \overline{21}\ \overline{17}$

$\overline{16}\ \overline{11}\ \overline{23}\ \overline{35}\ \overline{15}$ $\overline{17}\ \overline{31}\ \overline{14}\ \overline{35}$, $\overline{11}\ \overline{21}\ \overline{14}$

))

$\overline{46}\ \overline{26}\ \overline{36}\ \overline{13}\ \overline{27}\ \overline{13}\ \overline{34}\ \overline{11}\ \overline{16}\ \overline{36}$

GALATIANS 5:19-21
(CHILDREN'S BIBLE)

56

FIND THE WORDS BELOW IN THE WORDSEARCH PUZZLE.

WORSHIPING   ANGRY

ACTS   JEALOUSY

SINFUL   HATING

NATURE   LYING

FLESH   SHARING

```
A I T K S L F L E S H U G O
B W I I T S F R U T T N T D
O O E N C B E C L E I A G N
U R P D A N U L O Y D T C E
A S O N N N C E L N V U F S
B H A T I N G E D U T R T S
O I E N E B E R R E B E L N
U P P D T N U L Y J D U E C
A I O N N P C E D N F U F S
B N I E S H A R I N G K T S
C G E S J B E L I E B R G R
H E W S L B S S I C L T O T
N S J E A L O U S Y R O O L
```

THE BIBLE TELLS US HOW TO FIGHT THE DESIRES OF THE SINFUL NATURE.

USE THE CODE CHART BELOW TO MATCH THE CODES WITH LETTERS. USE THE COLUMN GOING DOWN, FIRST, THEN WRITE THE LETTERS IN THE BLANKS.

	1	2	3	4	5	6	7
4			Z	Y	X	W	V
3	O	P	Q	R	S	T	U
2	N	M	L	K	J	I	H
1	A	B	C	D	E	F	G

"
THOSE WHO BELONG TO
36 27 31 35 15   46 27 31   12 15 23 31 21 17   36 31

CHRIST JESUS HAVE
13 27 34 26 35 36   25 15 35 37 35   27 11 47 15

CRUCIFIED THE SINFUL
13 34 37 13 26 16 26 15 14   36 27 15   35 26 21 16 37 23

NATURE WITH ITS
21 11 36 37 34 15   46 26 36 27   26 36 35

PASSIONS AND DESIRES.
32 11 35 35 26 31 21 35   11 21 14   14 15 35 26 34 15 35

SINCE WE LIVE BY THE
35 26 21 13 15   46 15   23 26 47 15   12 44   36 27 15

SPIRIT, LET US KEEP
35 32 26 34 26 36)   23 15 36   37 35   24 15 15 32

IN STEP WITH THE
26 21   35 36 15 32   46 26 36 27   36 27 15

SPIRIT."   GALATIANS 5:24-25
35 32 26 34 26 36

58

FIND THE WORDS BELOW IN THE WORDSEARCH PUZZLE.

JESUS

SPIRIT

BELONG

PASSIONS

CRUCIFIED

STEP

DESIRES

KEEP

CHRIST

LIVE

```
L F L E S G H U O S F S E F
S F J E S U S T E S F R P T
B E C L E P A R N B E C A E
E U L O V D I D E N U L S Y
L C E L N S U R S N V U S F
O G E D E T R T I D U T I T
N E L D E B E L S T E P O L
G U L Y J D U C C Y J T N E
P C R U C I F I E D S F S F
H A R I N K K T S I N G K T
B E L E I E R G R I E B R G
B S L I V E T H T I C L T O
O U L S Y P C O L S Y R O O
```

MAKE YOUR WAY THROUGH THE MAZE.
WATCH OUT FOR DEAD ENDS, ESPECIALLY
SOME OF THE ACTS OF THE SINFUL NATURE.

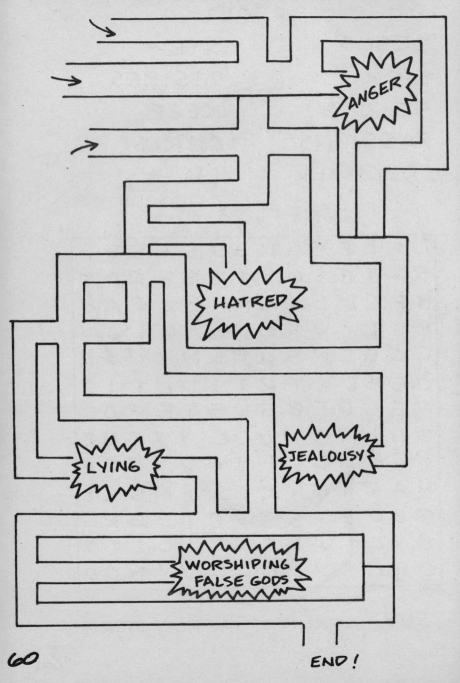

END!

FINISH THE FACE

YOU DO THE DRAWING! DRAW THE
EXPRESSION FOR JOY:

JOY— A FRUIT OF THE HOLY SPIRIT!

FINISH THE FACE

YOU DO THE DRAWING! DRAW THE
EXPRESSION FOR **PEACE**:

PEACE—A FRUIT OF THE HOLY SPIRIT!

FINISH THE FACE

YOU DO THE DRAWING! DRAW THE
EXPRESSION FOR **LOVE**:

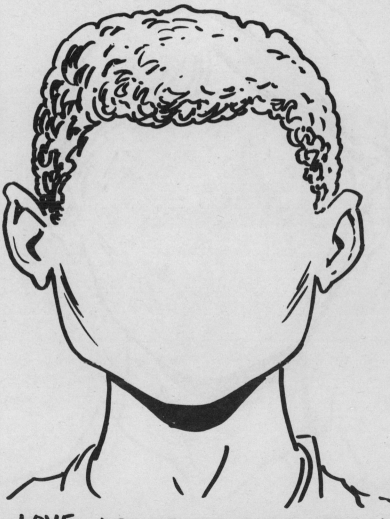

LOVE - A FRUIT OF THE HOLY SPIRIT!

FINISH THE FACE

YOU DO THE DRAWING! DRAW THE
EXPRESSION FOR **ANGER**:

ANGER- AN ACT OF THE SINFUL NATURE.

FINISH THE FACE

YOU DO THE DRAWING! DRAW THE
EXPRESSION FOR **HATRED**:

HATRED - AN ACT OF THE SINFUL NATURE.

65

THE THIRD ENEMY IN OUR LIVES WITH GOD
IS THE WORLD.

IT IS NOT THE WORLD IN ITSELF THAT IS
OUR ENEMY AS GOD CREATED THE WORLD.
IT IS SOME OF THE THINGS IN THE WORLD
THAT CAN LEAD US AWAY FROM GOD AND
WHAT HE WANTS US TO DO.

GO THROUGH THE MAZE.

CIRCLE THOSE THINGS THAT COULD BE USED
TO TEMPT YOU TO SIN AND TAKE YOU AWAY
FROM GOD'S PLAN FOR YOUR LIFE.
(YOU MAY BE SURPRISED!)

A LOT OF THINGS CAN
BE USED FOR BAD AS WELL
AS GOOD!

WHAT DOES GOD SAY ABOUT THE THINGS OF THE WORLD?

USE THE CODE CHART BELOW TO MATCH THE CODES WITH LETTERS. USE THE COLUMN GOING DOWN, FIRST, THEN WRITE THE LETTERS IN THE BLANKS.

	1	2	3	4	5	6	7
4			Z	Y	X	W	V
3	O	P	Q	R	S	T	U
2	N	M	L	K	J	I	H
1	A	B	C	D	E	F	G

"
$\overline{14}$ $\overline{31}$ $\overline{21}$ $\overline{31}$ $\overline{36}$ $\overline{23}$ $\overline{31}$ $\overline{47}$ $\overline{15}$ $\overline{36}$ $\overline{27}$ $\overline{15}$

$\overline{46}$ $\overline{31}$ $\overline{34}$ $\overline{23}$ $\overline{14}$ $\overline{31}$ $\overline{34}$ $\overline{11}$ $\overline{21}$ $\overline{44}$ $\overline{36}$ $\overline{27}$ $\overline{26}$ $\overline{21}$ $\overline{17}$

$\overline{26}$ $\overline{21}$ $\overline{36}$ $\overline{27}$ $\overline{15}$ $\overline{46}$ $\overline{31}$ $\overline{34}$ $\overline{23}$ $\overline{14}$, $\overline{26}$ $\overline{16}$

$\overline{11}$ $\overline{21}$ $\overline{44}$ $\overline{31}$ $\overline{21}$ $\overline{15}$ $\overline{23}$ $\overline{31}$ $\overline{47}$ $\overline{15}$ $\overline{35}$ $\overline{36}$ $\overline{27}$ $\overline{15}$

$\overline{46}$ $\overline{31}$ $\overline{34}$ $\overline{23}$ $\overline{14}$ ' $\overline{36}$ $\overline{27}$ $\overline{15}$ $\overline{23}$ $\overline{31}$ $\overline{47}$ $\overline{15}$ $\overline{31}$ $\overline{16}$

$\overline{36}$ $\overline{27}$ $\overline{15}$ $\overline{16}$ $\overline{11}$ $\overline{36}$ $\overline{27}$ $\overline{15}$ $\overline{34}$ $\overline{26}$ $\overline{35}$ $\overline{21}$ $\overline{31}$ $\overline{36}$

"
$\overline{26}$ $\overline{21}$ $\overline{27}$ $\overline{26}$ $\overline{22}$.   1 JOHN 2:15

68

UNSCRAMBLE THE UNDERLINED WORDS
AND PLACE THEM IN THE CORRECT SPACE
IN THE CROSSWORD GRID ON THE NEXT PAGE.

ACROSS

1. THE HOLY SPIRIT WILL LEAD YOU INTO ALL TUHRT.

2. YOUR YBDO IS THE TEMPLE OF THE HOLY SPIRIT.

3. YOU HAVE THREE ENEMIES. ONE OF THEM IS THE IVDEL.

4. ANOTHER OF YOUR ENEMIES IS YOUR FLESH, OR THE SINFUL AERTUN.

DOWN

5. THE HOLY SPIRIT IS ALSO CALLED THE LORSECNOU.

6. YOU ARE TO BE CHANGED BY THE RENEWING OF YOUR NMDI.

7. THE HOLY SPIRIT WILL PRODUCE GOD'S TFIUR IN YOU.

8. YOUR THIRD ENEMY IS THE THINGS OF THE RWLDO.

WORD LIST

MIND	DEVIL
BODY	NATURE
COUNSELOR	TRUTH
WORLD	FRUIT

69

70

EVEN THOUGH YOU ARE NOW GOD'S CHILD, YOU WILL STILL SIN. WHAT DO YOU DO THEN? TRAVEL THE PATH THAT MAKES A SENTENCE.

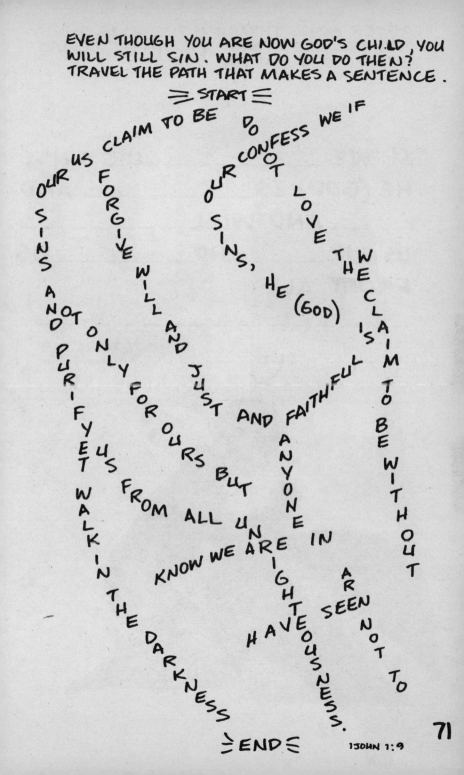

71

1 JOHN 1:9

AFTER GOING THROUGH THE MAZE ON THE PREVIOUS PAGE, FILL IN THE BLANKS BELOW TO FINISH THE VERSE.

"IF WE _____ OUR SINS, HE (GOD) IS _____ AND ____ AND WILL _____ US OUR ____ AND _____ US FROM ALL _____."

1 JOHN 1:9

FIND THE WORDS BELOW IN THE WORDSEARCH PUZZLE.

```
U F P D T P C O S P R R T I A
A L O N N F O R G I V E U T H
B L I E W A N T K N L A P D K
C N E S J I F I I W S F U U I
J W S E L T E E N E B E R L E
U S H S N H S P D T N U I O J
S S G E N F S O N N D C F D N
T I W S L U I E W S G Y T U
E W S G E L N E S J B E L B E
U N R I G H T E O U S N E S S
S L B S N N S H S N I B H A K
S N I B H S S G E N T L E N R
E N T L E H I W S L B P P I T
```

FORGIVE   SINS

FAITHFUL   JUST

PURIFY   CONFESS

UNRIGHTEOUSNESS

73

OUR LORD JESUS PAID THE PRICE FOR
OUR SINS. HE TOOK OUR PUNISHMENT
BY DYING ON THE CROSS.

USING THE GRID, DRAW THE PICTURE
BELOW ON THE NEXT PAGE.

ALL CHRISTIANS ARE TEMPTED TO SIN, TO DO THINGS THAT ARE WRONG. BUT WE CAN TRUST GOD TO HELP US IN OUR TIMES OF TEMPTATION.

USE THE CODE CHART BELOW TO MATCH THE CODES WITH LETTERS. USE THE COLUMN GOING DOWN, FIRST, THEN WRITE THE LETTERS IN THE BLANKS.

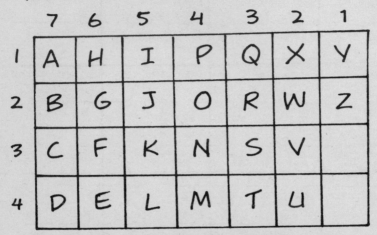

	7	6	5	4	3	2	1
1	A	H	I	P	Q	X	Y
2	B	G	J	O	R	W	Z
3	C	F	K	N	S	V	
4	D	E	L	M	T	U	

II

___ ___ ___   ___ ___ ___ ___
43 16 46   24 34 45 11

___ ___ ___ ___ ___ ___ ___ ___ ___ ___ ___
43 46 44 14 43 17 43 15 24 34 33

___ ___ ___ ___   ___ ___ ___   ___ ___ ___ ___
43 16 17 43   11 24 42   16 17 32 46

___ ___ ___   ___ ___ ___
17 23 46   43 16 46

___ ___ ___ ___ ___ ___ ___ ___ ___ ___ ___
43 46 44 14 43 17 43 15 24 34 33

___ ___ ___ ___   ___ ___ ___ ___ ___ ___ ___ ___
43 16 17 43   17 45 45 14 46 24 14 45 46

CONT'D NEXT PAGE . . .

16 17 32 46 • 27 42 43   11 24 42

37 17 34   43 23 42 33 43   26 24 47 •

16 46   22 15 45 45   34 24 43   45 46 43

11 24 42   27 46   43 46 44 14 43 46 47

44 24 23 46   43 16 17 34   11 24 42

37 17 34   33 43 17 34 47 •   27 42 43

22 16 46 34   11 24 42   17 23 46 ,

26 24 47   22 15 45 45   17 45 33 24

26 15 32 46   11 24 42   17   22 17 11

43 24   46 33 37 17 14 46   43 16 17 43

43 46 44 14 43 17   43 15 24 34 •

43 16 46 34   11 24 42   22 15 45 45

27 46   17 27 45 46   43 24

11

33 43 17 34 47   15 43 •

1 CORINTHIANS 10:13
(CHILDREN'S BIBLE)

CONNECT-THE-DOTS

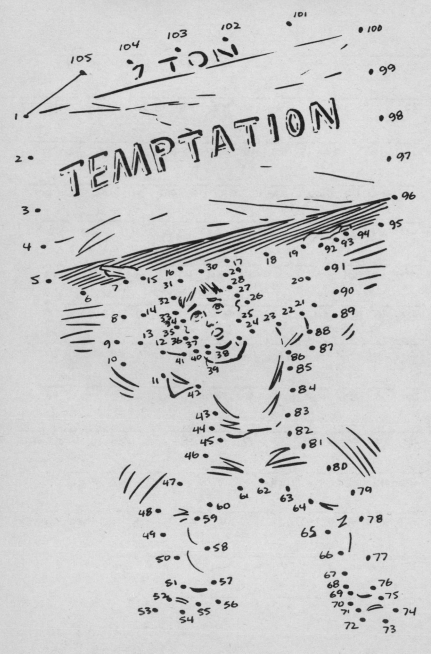

FIGHTING TEMPTATION ON YOUR OWN.

CONNECT-THE-DOTS

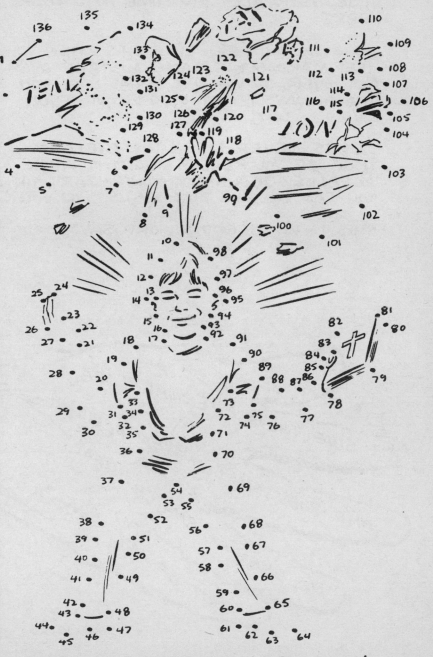

FIGHTING TEMPTATION WITH GOD!

SOMETIMES YOU MAY NOT FEEL LIKE YOU ARE A CHRISTIAN. YOU MAY EVEN WONDER IF JESUS REALLY DID COME INTO YOUR HEART.

USUALLY YOU FEEL LIKE THIS WHEN YOU KEEP MAKING THE SAME MISTAKE OVER AND OVER, OR WHEN IT SEEMS LIKE YOU ARE ALWAYS TEMPTED TO DO WHAT YOU KNOW IS SIN.

JESUS NEVER LIES; THE BIBLE IS TRUE. IF YOU REALLY MEANT IT WHEN YOU ASKED JESUS INTO YOUR HEART, THEN YOU CAN BELIEVE THAT JESUS IS IN YOU.

THIS IS WHAT GOD'S WORD SAYS:

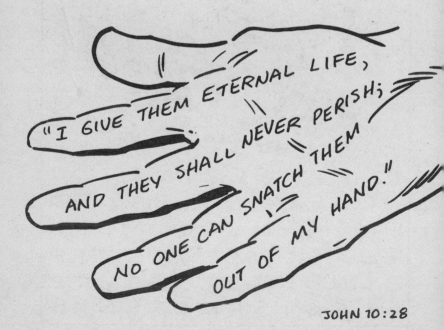

"I GIVE THEM ETERNAL LIFE, AND THEY SHALL NEVER PERISH; NO ONE CAN SNATCH THEM OUT OF MY HAND."

JOHN 10:28

THE ONLY WAY TO HEAVEN IS THROUGH
JESUS CHRIST. HAVING JESUS IN YOUR
HEART MEANS YOU HAVE BEEN GIVEN
ETERNAL LIFE, AND YOU WILL LIVE WITH
GOD FOREVER. THIS IS GOD'S PROMISE
TO YOU!

FIND THE UNDERLINED WORDS IN THE
WORD SEARCH PUZZLE BELOW.

"I GIVE THEM ETERNAL
LIFE, AND THEY SHALL NEVER
PERISH; NO ONE CAN SNATCH
THEM OUT OF MY HAND."

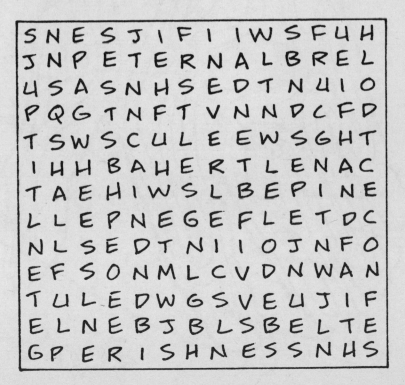

```
S N E S J I F I I W S F U H
J N P E T E R N A L B R E L
U S A S N H S E D T N U I O
P Q G T N F T V N N D C F D
T S W S C U L E E W S G H T
I H H B A H E R T L E N A C
T A E H I W S L B E P I N E
L L E P N E G E F L E T D C
N L S E D T N I I O J N F O
E F S O N M L C V D N W A N
T U L E D W G S V E U J I F
E L N E B J B L S B E L T E
G P E R I S H N E S S N H S
```

FROM THE START OF YOUR CHRISTIAN LIFE TO THE END OF IT, YOU WILL ALWAYS STAY IN THE HAND OF THE LORD JESUS.

LIFE WILL NOT ALWAYS BE EASY, BUT JESUS WILL GET YOU THROUGH!

FIND YOUR WAY THROUGH THE MAZE OF LIFE.

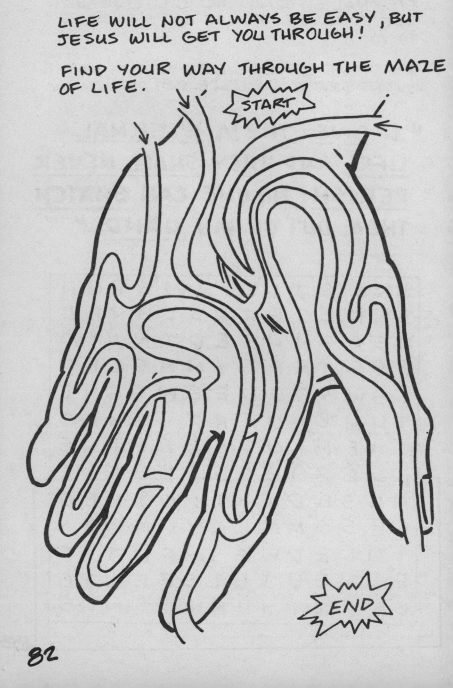

HOW TO DRAW THE HAND

STEP 1.

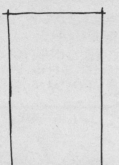

DRAW A RECTANGLE.

STEP 2.

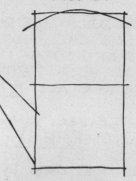

ADD A CONE SHAPE FOR THE THUMB, A LINE ACROSS THE MIDDLE, AND A CURVE ACROSS THE TOP.

STEP 3.

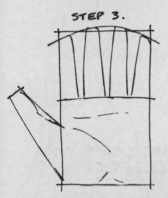

ADD FINGERS.

STEP 4.

FINISH BY ADDING DETAILS.

TRY IT FOR YOURSELF. YOU HAVE ROOM BELOW FOR TWO PICTURES. USE YOUR OWN HAND AS A GUIDE.

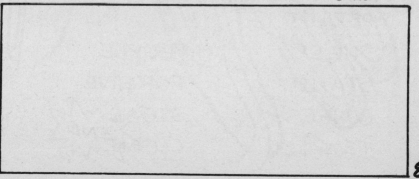

UNSCRAMBLE THE UNDERLINED WORDS
AND PLACE THEM IN THE CROSSWORD GRID
ON THE NEXT PAGE.

ACROSS

1. WE ARE TO <u>SSFCNOE</u> OUR SINS TO GOD.

2. WE ARE ALL <u>PTMTDEE</u> TO SIN.

3. THE BIBLE SAYS THAT PEOPLE ARE
   LIKE <u>PHESE</u>.

4. NO ONE CAN <u>ASETL</u> US OUT OF GOD'S
   HAND.

DOWN

1. GOD WILL MAKE OUR HEARTS
   <u>CLNAE</u> AND NEW.

2. GOD WILL <u>EFGRVOI</u> US FOR OUR
   SINS.

3. THE TEMPTATIONS THAT COME ARE
   WHAT COME TO ALL <u>EEPOLP</u>.

4. GOD WILL GIVE US A WAY TO ESCAPE
   TEMPTATION SO WE CAN <u>ASDNT</u>.

WORD LIST

SHEEP   PEOPLE
STAND   FORGIVE
CONFESS   STEAL
TEMPTED   CLEAN

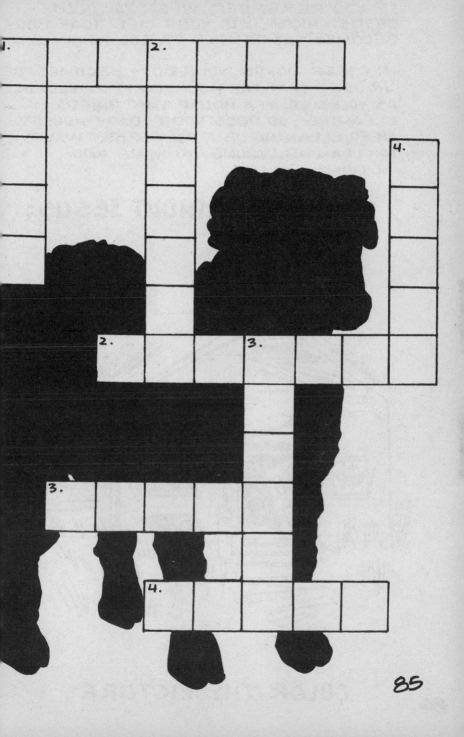

IF YOU REMEMBER, WHEN YOU INVITE
JESUS CHRIST INTO YOUR LIFE, YOUR BODY
BECOMES THE TEMPLE OF GOD'S HOLY SPIRI

IN OTHER WORDS, YOUR BODY BECOMES THE
"HOUSE" THAT THE HOLY SPIRIT DWELLS IN.
AS YOU LIVE IN A HOUSE THAT NEEDS
CLEANING, SO DOES YOUR "BODY-HOUSE"
NEED CLEANING. THE HOLY SPIRIT WANTS
TO CLEAN UP WRONG THINKING AND
ACTIONS.

THE HOUSE WITHOUT JESUS:

COLOR THE PICTURE.

NOW THAT THE HOLY SPIRIT LIVES IN YOU, HE IS GOING TO WANT TO CLEAN AND EVEN CHANGE SOME THINGS IN HIS HOUSE!

THIS TAKES TIME BUT THE RESULT IS THAT YOU ARE MADE FREE AND MUCH HAPPIER. AND JUST LIKE A NICE CLEAN HOUSE, YOU ARE MORE INVITING TO OTHERS. PEOPLE WILL WANT TO BE AROUND YOU, AND YOU CAN SHARE WITH THEM WHAT JESUS HAS DONE IN YOUR LIFE!

THE HOUSE WITH JESUS:

COLOR THE PICTURE.

GO THROUGH THE HOUSE BELOW AND
PICK UP THOSE THINGS THAT GOD WOULD
CLEAN OUT. WRITE THEM IN THE BLANK
SPACES BELOW.

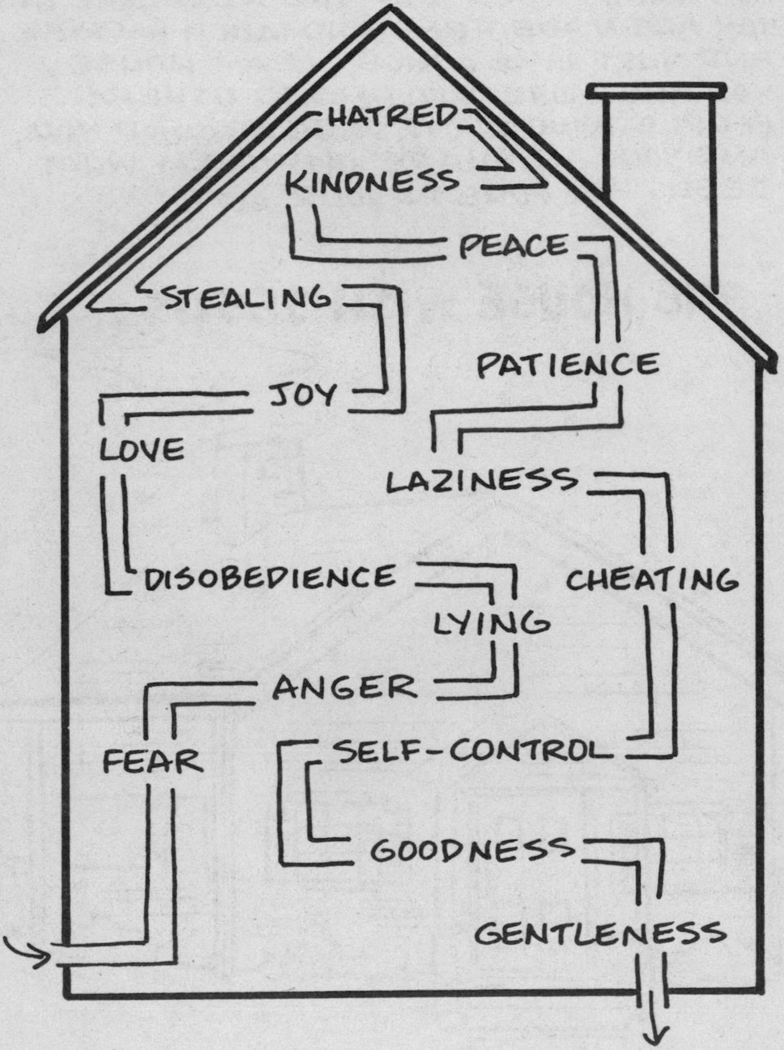

HATRED
KINDNESS
PEACE
STEALING
JOY
PATIENCE
LOVE
LAZINESS
DISOBEDIENCE
CHEATING
LYING
ANGER
SELF-CONTROL
FEAR
GOODNESS
GENTLENESS

_____   _____
_____   _____
_____   _____
_____   _____

AGAIN, IT IS THE WORK OF THE HOLY SPIRIT
THAT DOES THE CLEANING IN US. HE ONLY
NEEDS US TO BE WILLING TO LET HIM DO
THAT WORK.

GOD'S WORD GIVES US A PROMISE!

FIND THE UNDERLINED WORDS IN THE
WORDSEARCH PUZZLE BELOW.

"BE CONFIDENT OF THIS, THAT
HE WHO BEGAN A GOOD WORK
IN YOU WILL CARRY IT ON TO
THE FINISH UNTIL JESUS
CHRIST COMES AGAIN."

PHILIPPIANS 1:6
(CHILDREN'S BIBLE)

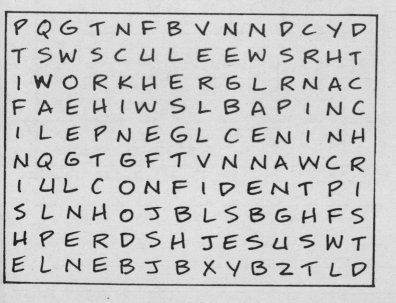

```
P Q G T N F B V N N D C Y D
T S W S C U L E E W S R H T
I W O R K H E R G L R N A C
F A E H I W S L B A P I N C
I L E P N E G L C E N I N H
N Q G T G F T V N N A W C R
I U L C O N F I D E N T P I
S L N H O J B L S B G H F S
H P E R D S H J E S U S W T
E L N E B J B X Y B Z T L D
```

PICTURE YOURSELF AS A SOLDIER!
YOU ARE NOW A SOLDIER FOR JESUS
CHRIST, AND HE GIVES US EVERYTHING
WE NEED TO WIN THE BATTLE.

USE THE CODE CHART BELOW TO MATCH
THE CODES WITH LETTERS. USE THE
COLUMN GOING DOWN FIRST, THEN WRITE
THE LETTERS IN THE BLANKS.

	1	2	3	4	5	6
5	A	F	K	P	U	Z
4	B	G	L	Q	V	
3	C	H	M	R	W	
2	D	I	N	S	X	
1	E	J	O	T	Y	

___ ___ ___ ___ ___ ___ ___ ' ___ ___
52 22 23 51 43 43 15   41 11

___ ___ ___ ___ ___ ___   ___ ___ ___ ___
24 14 34 13 23 42   22 23 14 32

___ ___ ___ ___ ___ ___ ___ ___ ___ ___ ___
43 13 34 21 51 23 21 22 23 32 22

___ ___ ___ ___ ___ ___   ___ ___ ___ ___ ___
33 22 42 32 14 15   54 13 35 11 3

90

CONT'E FROM PREVIOUS PAGE.

$\overline{54}$ $\overline{55}$ $\overline{14}$ $\overline{13}$ $\overline{23}$ $\overline{14}$ $\overline{32}$ $\overline{11}$ $\overline{52}$ $\overline{55}$ $\overline{43}$ $\overline{43}$

$\overline{51}$ $\overline{34}$ $\overline{33}$ $\overline{13}$ $\overline{34}$ $\overline{13}$ $\overline{52}$ $\overline{42}$ $\overline{13}$ $\overline{21}$

$\overline{24}$ $\overline{13}$ $\overline{14}$ $\overline{32}$ $\overline{51}$ $\overline{14}$ $\overline{15}$ $\overline{13}$ $\overline{55}$ $\overline{31}$ $\overline{51}$ $\overline{23}$

$\overline{14}$ $\overline{51}$ $\overline{53}$ $\overline{11}$ $\overline{15}$ $\overline{13}$ $\overline{55}$ $\overline{34}$ $\overline{24}$ $\overline{14}$ $\overline{51}$ $\overline{23}$ $\overline{21}$

$\overline{51}$ $\overline{42}$ $\overline{51}$ $\overline{22}$ $\overline{24}$ $\overline{23}$ $\overline{14}$ $\overline{14}$ $\overline{32}$ $\overline{11}$

$\overline{21}$ $\overline{11}$ $\overline{45}$ $\overline{22}$ $\overline{43}$ $\overline{24}$ $\overline{24}$ $\overline{31}$ $\overline{32}$ $\overline{11}$ $\overline{33}$ $\overline{11}$ $\overline{24}$.

EPHESIANS 6:10-11

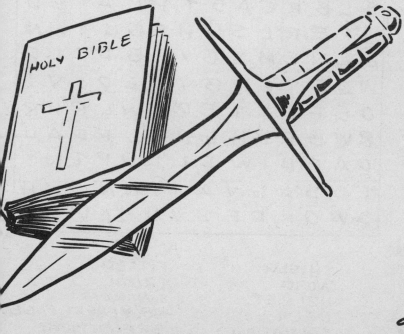

FIND THE UNDERLINED WORDS IN THE WORDSEARCH PUZZLE BELOW.

" STAND FIRM THEN, WITH THE <u>BELT</u> OF
<u>TRUTH</u> BUCKLED AROUND YOUR WAIST,
WITH THE <u>BREAST PLATE</u> OF RIGHTEOUSNES
IN PLACE , AND WITH YOUR FEET <u>FITTED</u> WITH
THE READINESS THAT COMES FROM THE
<u>GOSPEL</u> OF PEACE . IN ADDITION TO ALL
THIS, TAKE UP THE <u>SHIELD</u> OF FAITH, WITH
WHICH YOU CAN EXTINGUISH ALL THE
FLAMING ARROWS OF THE EVIL ONE. TAKE
THE <u>HELMET</u> OF <u>SALVATION</u> AND THE
<u>SWORD</u> OF THE SPIRIT, WHICH IS THE
<u>WORD</u> OF GOD. "

EPHESIANS 6: 14 - 17

THIS IS THE FULL ARMOR OF GOD!

```
I U L C H N F I G O S P E L
S L B R E A S T P L A T E D
H P E R L S H H E S U T W N
E L N E M J B X I B L T L D
W Q G T E F B V N E D C Y T
O S F I T T E D B W L R H R
R W B R K H E R G L R D A U
D A E H I W S L B D P T W T
I L S A L V A T I O N I N H
S W O R D F T V N N A W C R
```

SHIELD   FITTED
WORD   TRUTH
HELMET   SWORD
BELT   GOSPEL
SALVATION   BREASTPLATE

92

FILL IN THE BLANKS.

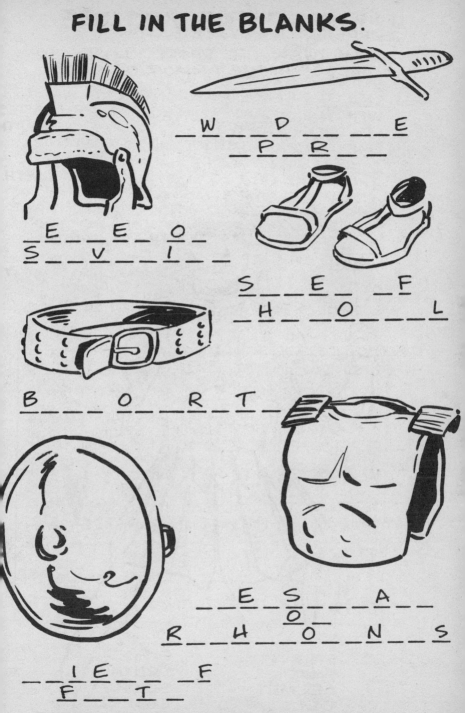

_ W _ _ D _ _ _ _ E
_ P _ R _
S _ _ V _ _ I _ _ _
E   E   O
S _ _ E _ _ F
H   O   L
B _ _ _ O _ R _ T _

_ _ E _ S _ _ _ A _ _
R _ H _ O _ N _ _ S
_ _ I E _ _ _ F
F _ _ T _

THE FULL ARMOR OF GOD! 93

FINISH THE PICTURE.

DRAW OVER THE DOTTED LINES TO "DRESS" IN THE ARMOR OF GOD.

FIND YOUR WAY THROUGH THE BATTLEFIELD OF LIFE. WATCH OUT FOR TEMPTATION AND SIN!

END

DO YOU REMEMBER OUR THREE ENEMIES,
THE *WORLD*, THE *FLESH* (OR SINFUL NATURE),
AND THE *DEVIL*?

WE CALL THE BATTLE AGAINST THESE
ENEMIES SPIRITUAL WARFARE!

GOD'S WORD HAS SOMETHING TO SAY
ABOUT THIS WARFARE.

" FOR OUR STRUGGLE (OUR BATTLE) IS
NOT AGAINST FLESH AND BLOOD, BUT
AGAINST THE RULERS, AGAINST THE
AUTHORITIES, AGAINST THE POWERS OF
THIS DARK WORLD AND AGAINST THE
SPIRITUAL FORCES OF EVIL IN THE
HEAVENLY REALMS (THE UNSEEN
SPIRITUAL WORLD AROUND US)."

EPHESIANS 6:12

FIND THE WORDS BELOW IN THE WORDSEARCH.

```
      C H B F L G O
    L B R E F L E S H
    E B R L I H O E S U
S E L N T V J B X O B
  T Q G E W F B V W D C Y
D P R F L T O S D P X D
  R A U T H O R I T I E S
W D N H G V W S L B D P T W
  P L S A G V D T D N Z H
H E A V E N L Y V G J Q C R
  L N R U L E R S W L
    B R K H S N G L R
    H W   L
```

FLESH   RULERS

EVIL   BLOOD

WORLD   HEAVENLY

STRUGGLE   AUTHORITIES

NOW IT IS TIME TO START LIVING YOUR
LIFE AS A CHILD OF GOD.

THERE ARE MANY THINGS IN LIFE THAT
CAN DISTRACT US, OR LEAD US AWAY,
FROM JESUS.

WHAT DOES JESUS SAY WE SHOULD DO?

UNSCRAMBLE THE WORDS AND PUT
THEM IN THE RIGHT PLACES IN THE
VERSE BELOW.

" LET US <u>XFI</u> OUR EYES ON <u>SEUJS</u>,
THE <u>RATUHO</u> AND PERFECTER OF
OUR <u>AFHIT</u>, WHO FOR THE <u>OYJ</u> SET
<u>EBRFEO</u> HIM ENDURED THE <u>ORSCS</u>,
SCORNING ITS <u>MHSEA</u>, AND SAT
<u>WODN</u> AT THE RIGHT <u>NDHA</u> OF THE
<u>HTNROE</u> OF GOD."

                              HEBREWS 12:2

" LET US_____ OUR EYES ON

_____,THE _____ AND

PERFECTER OF OUR _____,

WHO FOR THE ___ SET_____

HIM ENDURED THE _____,

SCORNING ITS_____,AND SAT

_____ AT THE RIGHT _____ OF

THE _____OF GOD."

CREATION

GENESIS 1:1 - 2:3

ACROSS

1) ON THE 7ᵗʰ DAY GOD _____.
2) GOD MADE MAN FROM _____.
3) GOD MADE _____ FIRST.
4) MADE IN GOD'S IMAGE.

DOWN

1) EVE WAS MADE FROM ADAM'S _____.
5) THE FIRST WOMAN
6) THE GARDEN OF _____.
7) GOD CREATED EVERYTHING IN _____ DAYS.
8) THE FIRST MAN.

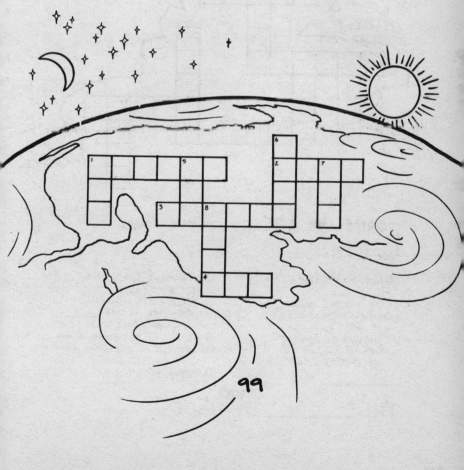

99

CAIN AND ABEL   GENESIS 4:1-17

ACROSS

1) ABEL WAS SHEPHERD OVER HIS _____.
2) CAIN WAS A _____.
3) CAIN'S FIRST SON WAS NAMED _____.
4) CAIN WAS SO ANGRY THAT HE _____ HIS BROTHER ABEL.

DOWN

5) CAIN ASKED GOD, "AM I MY BROTHER'S _____?".
6) AFTER ABEL'S MURDER, CAIN AND HIS WIFE _____ FAR AWAY FROM ADAM & EVE.
7) ADAM & EVE'S SECOND SON.
8) GOD PUT A _____ ON CAIN TO PROTECT HIM.
9) ADAM & EVE'S FIRST SON.

100

ANIMALS ON THE ARK

GENESIS 7:8

ACROSS

1) LARGE, STRONG CATTLE -
   "STRONG AS AN ___"
2) SMALL RODENT THAT
   LIKES CHEESE.
3) HAS A POCKET AND HOPS
4) HAS A LONG NECK
5) HAS A HORN
   ON ITS NOSE
6) FASTEST ANIMAL
   ON LAND

DOWN

2) PRIMATES WITH TAILS
7) A _____ RETURNED TO
   NOAH WITH AN OLIVE
   BRANCH.
8) LARGE, WILD DOG
9) HOPS AND HAS BIG EARS,
   LOVES CARROTS
10) THE "KING OF BEASTS"
11) HAS A HUMP ON ITS BACK
12) LARGE, FLIGHTLESS BIRD

101

TOWER
OF
BABEL

GENESIS 11:1-9

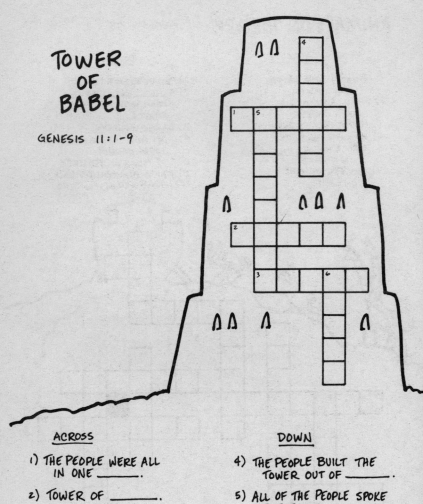

ACROSS

1) THE PEOPLE WERE ALL
   IN ONE _____.

2) TOWER OF _____.

3) GOD WANTED THE
   PEOPLE TO LIVE
   ALL OVER THE _____.

DOWN

4) THE PEOPLE BUILT THE
   TOWER OUT OF _____.

5) ALL OF THE PEOPLE SPOKE
   THE SAME _____

6) THE PEOPLE WANTED THE
   _____ TO REACH
   HIGH TO HEAVEN.

CANAAN, THE NEW LAND

GENESIS 13:5-18

ACROSS

1) THERE WAS NOT ENOUGH GREEN _____ FOR ALL THE SHEEP AND CATTLE TO EAT.

2) ABRAM + LOT COULD NOT _____ THE SAME LAND.

3) LOT WENT TO LIVE NEAR THE _____ RIVER.

DOWN

2) LOT WENT TO LIVE IN THIS WICKED CITY.

4) THE NEW LAND GOD BROUGHT ABRAM TO.

5) ABRAM AND LOT HAD FLOCKS OF THESE WOOLY ANIMALS.

6) ABRAM'S NEPHEW.

103

ABRAM BECOMES ABRAHAM

GENESIS 16, 17

ACROSS

1) ABRAM'S NEW NAME.

2) A MESSENGER FROM GOD.

3) GOD SAID SARAH WOULD HAVE A _____ BOY.

DOWN

4) ABRAHAM'S WIFE'S NEW NAME.

5) SARAH'S HANDMAID.

6) GOD SAID ABRAHAM WOULD BE THE FATHER OF _____ NATIONS.

7) _____ PROMISED ABRAHAM HE WOULD GIVE HIM A SON, A PEOPLE AND A LAND.

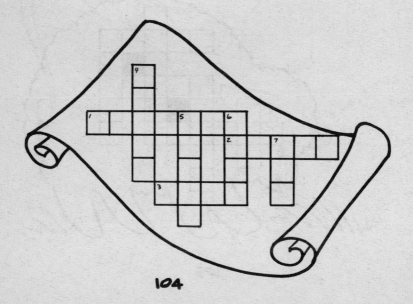

ISHMAEL

GENESIS 16-21

ACROSS

1) HAGAR & ISHMAEL BECAME
   LOST IN THE _____.
2) ISHMAEL BECAME A
   SKILLED _____
   WHEN HE WAS GROWN.
3) OPPOSITE OF SHORT.
4) BOW AND _____.

DOWN

5) ABRAHAM WAS ____ WHEN HE
   SENT HAGAR AWAY, UNHAPPY.
6) HAGAR'S SON
7) SARAH'S HANDMAID,
   ISHMAEL'S MOTHER.

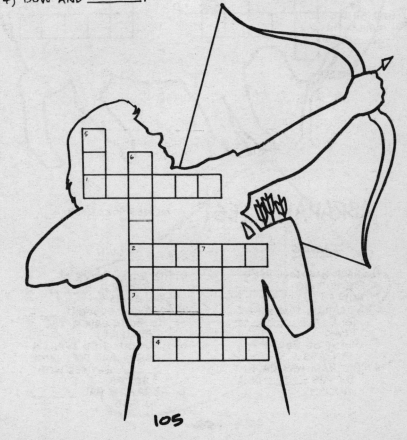

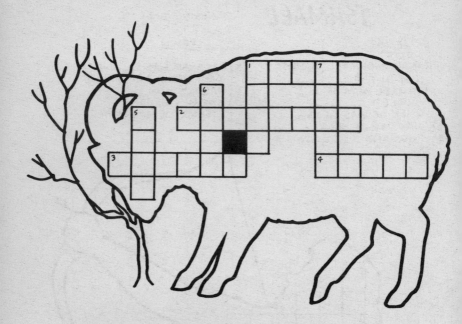

ABRAHAM'S TEST

GENESIS 22:1-13

ACROSS

1) SHARP HANDTOOL USED FOR CUTTING; _____ AND FORK.
2) ABRAHAM TOOK ISAAC TO A TALL _____ PEAK.
3) BEAST OF BURDEN, AN ASS.
4) THE RAM WAS CAUGHT BY HIS _____ IN A THICKET.

DOWN

1) THE ROYAL RULER OF A COUNTRY, "_____ OF KINGS".
5) ABRAHAM BROUGHT _____ TO BURN UNDER THE SACRIFICE.
6) ABRAHAM TIED ISAAC'S HANDS AND FEET WITH _____. RHYMES WITH "HOPE".
7) ABRAHAM HAD _____ IN GOD.

106

JACOB AND ESAU   GENESIS 25:24-34

ACROSS

1) _____ AND ARROW
2) JACOB WAS A _____ MAN, NOT NOISY.
3) ESAU _____ DEER WITH HIS BOW AND ARROW.
4) COVERED WITH LOTS OF HAIR.
5) THE YOUNGER TWIN BORN TO ISAAC AND REBEKAH.
6) JACOB GRABBED ESAU'S _____ AS THEY WERE BORN.

DOWN

1) ESAU SOLD JACOB HIS _____ FOR SOME FOOD.
7) THE OLDER OF THE TWINS.
8) REBEKAH BORE _____ BOYS.
9) JACOB AND ESAU'S MOTHER
10) FIRST AND LAST LETTERS OF THE WORD "USUALLY".

107

JACOB'S FAMILY

GENESIS 29,30

ACROSS

1) JACOB'S UNCLE

2) JACOB'S FIRST WIFE

3) JACOB HAD HOW MANY SONS?

4) RACHEL LOVED HER HUSBAND, _____.

DOWN

5) JACOB'S SECOND WIFE

6) JACOB'S OLDER TWIN BROTHER

7) JACOB AND RACHEL'S FIRST SON

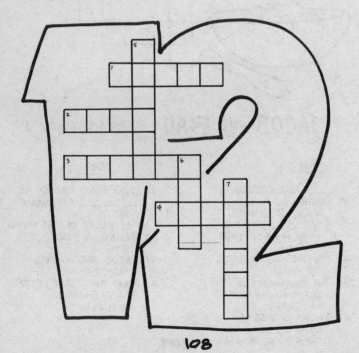

108

YOUNG JOSEPH

GENESIS 35:16-37

ACROSS

1) JACOB _____ JOSEPH WITH ALL OF HIS HEART.

2) JOSEPH'S FATHER

3) A COAT HAS HOW MANY SLEEVES?

4) JOSEPH HAD HOW MANY OLDER BROTHERS? (THE NUMBER AFTER NINE)

DOWN

5) JOSEPH WAS A YOUNG _____. RHYMES WITH "TOY".

6) JACOB'S YOUNGEST SON

7) "COAT OF MANY _____"

8) JACOB GAVE JOSEPH A SPECIAL, COLORFUL _____.

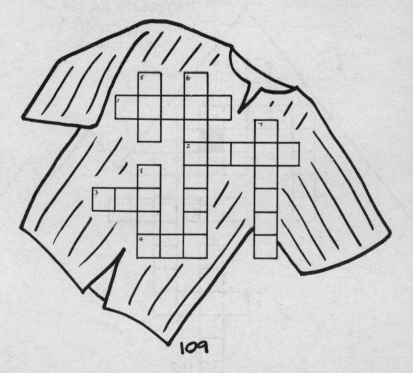

109

JOSEPH IN EGYPT

GENESIS 39, 40

ACROSS

1) HIGH-RANKING MANSERVANT

2) PHARAOH RULED OVER _____.

3) VISIONS DURING SLEEP

4) GOD WAS _____ JOSEPH.

DOWN

1) ONE WHO BAKES

5) OPPOSITE OF COLD

6) NOT THE TRUTH

7) _____ OF SUNLIGHT; X-_____

8) KING OF EGYPT

9) JOSEPH WAS PUT IN _____ FOR A CRIME HE DID NOT COMMIT.

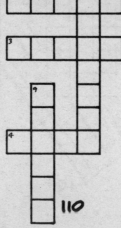

110

JOSEPH'S BROTHERS VISIT GENESIS 42-44

ACROSS

1) JOSEPH'S YOUNGER
   BROTHER

2) JOSEPH'S BROTHERS
   CAME TO BUY _____
   TO FEED THEIR FAMILY.

3) AS SECOND IN COMMAND,
   JOSEPH _____
   OVER EGYPT.

DOWN

4) WE USE _____ TO
   BUY THINGS.

5) A TIME OF NO FOOD, HUNGER

6) JOSEPH'S FATHER

7) OPPOSITE OF WET

8) WHAT NUMBER COMES
   AFTER NINE?

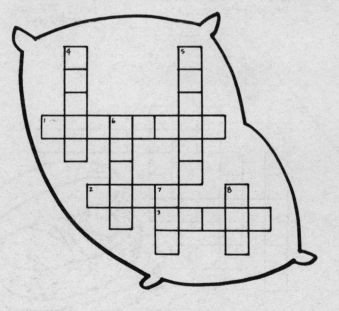

111

BABY MOSES

EXODUS 2:1-10

ACROSS

1) THE DAUGHTER OF A KING IS CALLED A _____.

2) MOSES' _____ WATCHED AS HER BROTHER FLOATED DOWN THE RIVER.

3) MOSES BECAME PHARAOH'S DAUGHTER'S _____.

DOWN

4) MOSES FLOATED DOWN THE RIVER IN A STRAW _____.

5) THE PRINCESS NAMED HER ADOPTED SON _____.

6) OPPOSITE OF DOWN

7) LONG, FLOWING WATERWAY.

112

PLAGUES OF EGYPT

EXODUS 7:14 - 10:29

ACROSS

1) THE RIVER WAS TURNED INTO _____ .

2) SMALL PARASITIC BUGS RHYMES WITH "NICE"

3) LEAPING AMPHIBIANS

4) OPPOSITE OF LIGHT

5) SWARMS OF GRASSHOPPERS

9) DIRTY, FLYING INSECT PESTS RHYMES WITH "PIES"

DOWN

3) FLAMES

6) RAW SORES ON THE SKIN

7) OPPOSITE OF HEALTHY .

8) FROZEN BITS OF ICE FALLING FROM THE SKY DESTROYING CROPS

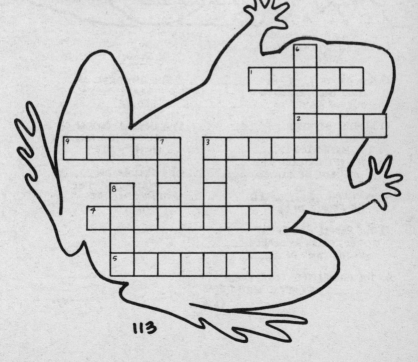

113

THE EXODUS

EXODUS 13:17-22

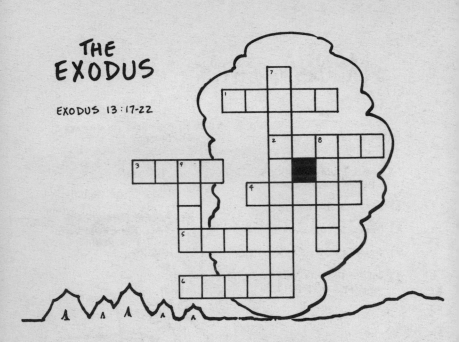

ACROSS

1) GOD CHOSE _____ TO
   LEAD THE ISRAELITES
   OUT OF EGYPT.

2) MOSES' BROTHER

3) THE ISRAELITES _____
   EGYPT QUICKLY. THE
   OPPOSITE OF STAYED.

4) A PILLAR OF _____ LED
   THE PEOPLE BY DAY.

5) THE PEOPLE HAD SPENT
   400 YEARS AS SLAVES
   IN THE LAND OF _____.

6) THE ISRAELITES TOOK THEIR
   _____ OF CATTLE WITH THEM.

DOWN

7) THE CHILDREN OF
   ISRAEL, GOD'S
   PEOPLE

8) A CERTAIN COURSE OF
   A JOURNEY. RHYMES
   WITH "POUT"

9) A PILLAR OF _____
   WAS WITH THE
   PEOPLE AT
   NIGHT.

MANNA

EXODUS 16

DOWN

2) THE ISRAELITES COULD
   _____ THE MANNA
   INTO BREAD.
3) EACH _____ THE PEOPLE
   HAD MANNA TO EAT.
4) GROUND BIRDS GOD
   PROVIDED FOR MEAT
5) GOD GAVE THE
   PEOPLE ENOUGH
   _____ TO
   DRINK.

ACROSS

1) FOOD THAT FELL FROM HEAVEN
   FROM GOD
2) TO COOK SOMETHING IN
   BUBBLING HOT WATER
3) A BARREN, DRY LAND

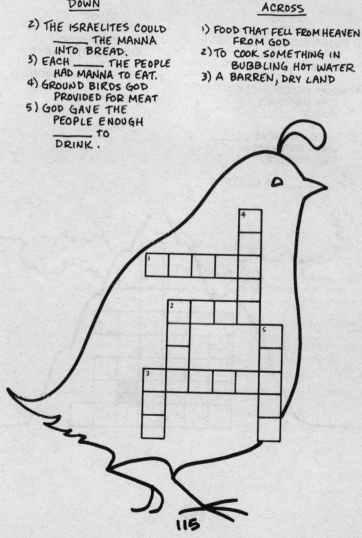

115

MOSES ON MT. SINAI

ACROSS

1) MOSES CLIMBED ALL THE
   WAY TO THE _____
   OF MT. SINAI.

2) MOSES RECEIVED THE 10
   COMMANDMENTS ON
   MOUNT _____.

3) THE PEOPLE WERE _____
   WHEN THEY HEARD
   THE THUNDER.

4) _____ AND LIGHTNING

DOWN

2) OPPOSITE OF STOP-
   RHYMES WITH "PART"

5) A TALL PEAK OF LAND

6) A FEMALE DEER

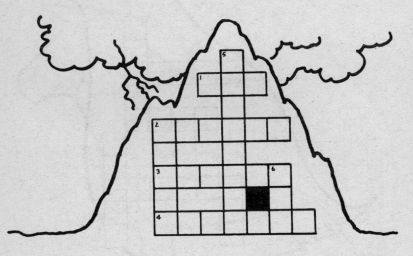

THE GOLDEN CALF

EXODUS 32

ACROSS

1) MOSES' BROTHER WHO MADE THE GOLDEN CALF

2) A FALSE GOD

3) MOSES _____ THE STONE TABLETS WHEN HE SAW THE PEOPLE WORSHIPING THE GOLDEN CALF. (RHYMES WITH "CROAK")

DOWN

4) TO BREAK GOD'S LAW IS _____.

5) A BABY COW

6) THE PEOPLE'S SIN MADE GOD _____. (MAD)

7) THE _____ CALF

THE PRIESTS

EXODUS 28

ACROSS

1) ONLY A PRIEST COULD ENTER THE _____ PLACE.

2) GOD SAID NOT TO _____ IDOLS

3) THE PRIESTS WERE BAREFOOT, NOTHING ON THEIR _____.

4) GOD CHOSE AARON AND HIS _____ TO BE THE PRIESTS.

DOWN

5) MOSES' BROTHER, HIGH PRIEST

6) ONLY MEN FROM THE TRIBE OF _____ COULD BE PRIESTS

7) AARON AND HIS SONS WERE _____.

8) OPPOSITE OF FROM- RHYMES WITH "DO"

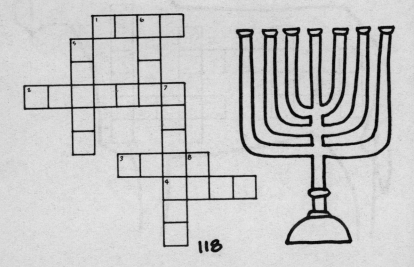

118

BALAAM

NUMBERS 22

ACROSS

1) BALAAM ___ HIS DONKEY WITH A STICK.

2) AN ___ OF GOD STOOD IN BALAAM'S WAY.

3) BALAAM'S ___ COULD SEE THE ANGEL. (AN ASS)

4) THE ANGEL HELD A SHARP ___.

DOWN

5) ___ DID NOT WANT BALAAM TO CURSE HIS CHOSEN PEOPLE (THE LORD).

6) THE DONKEY ___ TO BALAAM! (RHYMES WITH "WALKED")

7) THE DONKEY CRUSHED BALAAM'S FOOT AGAINST A ___. (RHYMES WITH "BALL")

119

CROSSING THE JORDAN

JOSHUA 3

ACROSS

1) THE _____ OF THE COVENANT

2) THE NATION OF ISRAEL HAD HOW MANY TRIBES?

3) THE PEOPLE CROSSED THE JORDAN RIVER ON _____ LAND.

4) ROCKS

DOWN

5) THE LEVITE _____ CARRIED THE ARK OF THE COVENANT.

6) THE _____ IN THE RIVER JORDAN PARTED TO ALLOW THE PEOPLE TO PASS ON DRY LAND.

7) THE PRIESTS AND ARK _____ THE PEOPLE ACROSS THE RIVER FIRST. (RHYMES WITH BED)

120

THE WALLS OF JERICHO FALL

JOSHUA 6

ACROSS

1) THE PEOPLE MARCHED _____ THE CITY.

2) THE TRUMPETS WERE MADE FROM _____ HORNS. (MALE SHEEP)

3) THE WALLS OF THIS CITY FELL.

4) AS PROMISED, RAHAB'S FAMILY WAS KEPT _____ THROUGH THE BATTLE.

5) THE PEOPLE'S SHOUT MADE THE _____ OF JERICHO FALL.

DOWN

6) THE PRIESTS BLEW THESE INSTRUMENTS.

7) THE PEOPLE DID _____ WITH A LOUD VOICE.

8) AS GOD SAID THEY WOULD, THE WALLS OF JERICHO _____ .

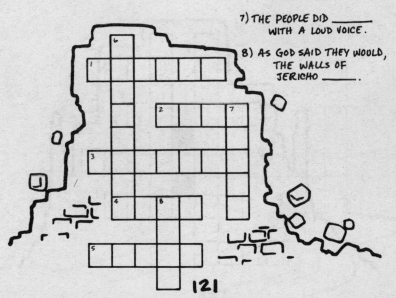

CALEB'S VICTORY

JOSHUA 14

ACROSS

1) CALEB WAS NOT YOUNG. HE WAS _____.

2) CALEB WAS NOT WEAK, BUT VERY _____.

3) _____ LED HIS ARMY TO VICTORY OVER THE CITY OF HEBRON.

4) HUGE, TALL PEOPLE

5) A GROUP OF SOLDIERS UNDER THE SAME COMMAND

DOWN

6) CALEB WAS 85 _____ OLD.

7) TALL PEAK OF LAND

8) A LARGE TOWN — RHYMES WITH "PRETTY"

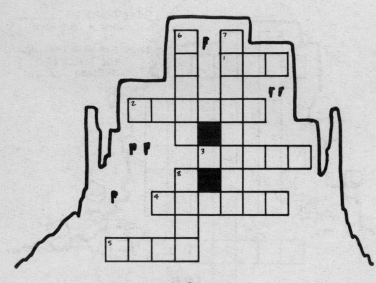

122

JOSHUA'S WORDS

JOSHUA 23, 24

ACROSS

1) JOSHUA WARNED THE PEOPLE NOT TO ____ THEIR PROMISE TO GOD.

2) THE PEOPLE PROMISED THAT THEY WOULD SERVE THE ____.

3) " ____ AND ORDER "

DOWN

4) JOSHUA SET UP A HUGE ____ AS A MONUMENT. (ROCK)

5) OPPOSITE OF NONE

6) JOSHUA WROTE DOWN THE PEOPLE'S PROMISE IN THE ____ OF THE LAW.

7) JOSHUA SAID, "DON'T WORSHIP ____. " (FALSE GODS)

DEBORAH THE JUDGE

JUDGES 4:4,5

ACROSS

1) DEBORAH WAS A _____ OVER ISRAEL (RHYMES WITH "NUDGE").

2) SHE WOULD _____ UNDER A PALM TREE.

3) THE ONLY WOMAN JUDGE TO RULE OVER THE ISRAELITES.

4) IF YOU ARE WISE, YOU ARE FULL OF _____. (GOOD JUDGEMENT)

DOWN

5) DEBORAH GAVE GOOD _____ TO HOSE WHO CAME TO HER SEEKING COUNSEL (ENDS WITH "ICE").

6) OPPOSITE OF BAD

7) DEBORAH SAT UNDER A _____ TREE. (RHYMES WITH "CALM")

124

GIDEON'S VICTORY

JUDGES 7

ACROSS

1) USED FOR LIGHT IN THE DARKNESS (RHYMES WITH CAMP)

2) GIDEON'S SOLDIERS BLEW THEIR _____.

7) A BIRD HATCHES FROM AN ____.

DOWN

3) GIDEON'S 300 MEN DEFEATED THE MIGHTY MIDIANITE ____ IN BATTLE.

4) A CONTAINER FOR HOLDING AND POURING WATER

5) BRAVERY

6) GIDEON'S VICTORY WAS WON WITH ONLY 300 STRONG ____.

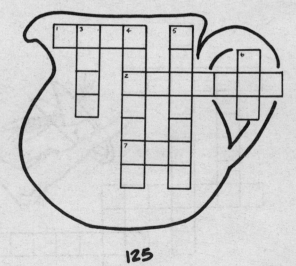

125

SAMSON & DELILAH

JUDGES 15,16

ACROSS

1) SAMSON WAS VERY
   _____, NOT WEAK.

2) THE WOMAN WHO LEARNED
   THE SOURCE OF SAMSON'S
   STRENGTH, THEN
   BETRAYED HIM

3) LARGE, VERTICAL COLUMNS
   IN A BUILDING, RHYMES
   WITH "FILLERS"

DOWN

4) THE KING OF BEASTS,
   SAMSON KILLED ONE

5) SAMSON DESTROYED THE
   PHILISTINE _____
   BY KNOCKING DOWN
   ITS PILLARS.

6) NOT ABLE TO SEE

7) DELILAH CUT SAMSON'S
   _____ DESTROYING
   HIS STRENGTH.

126

HANNAH'S PROMISE 1 SAMUEL 1

ACROSS

1) GOD ANSWERED HANNAH'S PRAYER FOR A _____ BOY

2) HANNAH WAS SAD BECAUSE SHE HAD NO _____. (KIDS)

3) TO TALK TO GOD

9) SMALL DRINKING CONTAINERS RHYMES WITH "PUPS"

DOWN

4) HANNAH'S SON

5) OPPOSITE OF NO

6) OPPOSITE OF HE

7) GOD _____ HIS PROMISES.

8) WEEP

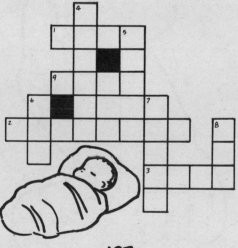

127

GOD CALLS SAMUEL

I SAMUEL 3:1-18

ACROSS

1) TO QUESTION, RHYMES WITH "TASK"

2) WHAT WE DO AT NIGHT WHEN WE'RE TIRED

3) THE PRIEST WHO CARED FOR SAMUEL

4) WE SLEEP IN A _____.

5) OPPOSITE OF STOP

DOWN

4) OPPOSITE OF GIRL

6) SAMUEL HEARD GOD CALL HIS _____ FOUR TIMES

7) GOD _____ SAMUEL BY NAME THAT NIGHT. (RHYMES WITH "WALLED")

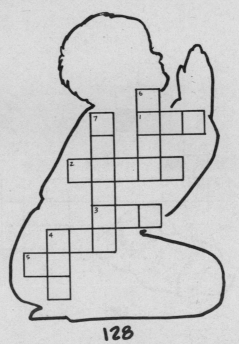

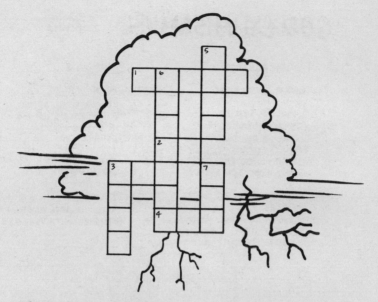

SAMUEL PRAYS
FOR VICTORY

I SAMUEL 7:1-14

ACROSS

1) VIOLENT WEATHER
   DISTURBANCE –
   RHYMES WITH "FORM"

2) OPPOSITE OF YES

3) OPPOSITE OF GOOD

4) THE PHILISTINES
   WERE AFRAID AND
   _____ AWAY.

DOWN

3) THE PHILISTINES FLED
   AND NEVER CAME
   _____.

5) TO TALK TO GOD

6) _____ AND LIGHTNING

7) WITH GOD'S HELP, THE
   ISRAELITES _____
   THE BATTLE.
   (VICTORY)

129

SAUL'S MISTAKES

1 SAMUEL 13,14

ACROSS

1) A GROUP OF SOLDIERS

2) A SWEET SYRUP BEES MAKE

3) SAUL COMMANDED HIS ARMY NOT TO _____ ANY FOOD FOR A DAY.

4) SAUL'S SOLDIERS WERE WEAK AND _____ FROM FIGHTING AND NOT EATING. (RHYMES WITH "FIRED")

DOWN

5) ONLY A _____ WAS ALLOWED TO OFFER SACRIFICES OR GO INTO THE HOLY OF HOLIES.

6) A STAND OF MANY TREES

7) A PERSON _____ TO EAT FOOD TO HAVE ENERGY. (RHYMES WITH "SEEDS")

130

DAVID FIGHTS GOLIATH

1 SAMUEL 17

ACROSS

1) THE SPIRIT OF ____ WAS WITH DAVID.

2) HOW MANY STONES DID DAVID CHOOSE FOR HIS SLING? (THE NUMBER AFTER FOUR)

3) A PIECE OF ARMOR (RHYMES WITH "FIELD")

4) THE PHILISTINE GIANT

5) GOLIATH WAS NINE FEET ____.

6) THE FIRST WOMAN GOD CREATED

DOWN

3) DAVID'S WEAPON

7) "____ AND GOLIATH"

8) GOD WAS ____ DAVID

9) DAVID ____ GOLIATH WITH HIS OWN SWORD. (SLEW)

10) DAVID HURLED A ____ AT THE GIANTS FOREHEAD.

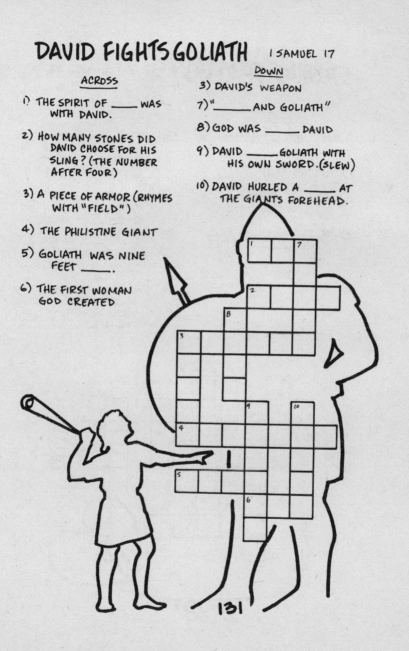

131

SAUL'S JEALOSY

I SAMUEL 18:5-16

ACROSS

1) DAVID HAD GREAT COURAGE, HE WAS _____.

2) TO HAVE FEAR

3) KING _____ WAS JEALOUS OF DAVID.

4) IN THE MORNING THE SUN _____. (COMES UP)

DOWN

5) TO BE ENVIOUS

6) ATTEMPT- RHYMES WITH "CRY"

7) SAUL WAS AFRAID DAVID WOULD TRY TO BE _____ INSTEAD OF HIM.

8) SAUL WAS OFTEN _____. (MAD)

9) THE TWO LIMBS THAT GO FROM THE SHOULDERS TO THE HANDS

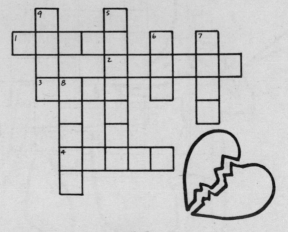

DAVID HIDES

I SAMUEL 21, 22

ACROSS

1) OPPOSITE OF IN

2) THE PRIEST GAVE DAVID LOAVES OF _____.

3) DAVID'S ARMY HAD 400 BRAVE _____.

4) WITHOUT FOOD DAVID BECAME _____.

DOWN

5) THE GIANT WHO DAVID SLEW

6) BATH _____ (RHYMES WITH "RUB")

7) DAVID HID IN A _____. (RHYMES WITH "SAVE")

8) A GROUP OF SOLDIERS

9) JEWELRY YOU WEAR ON A FINGER.

10) LONG, SHARP, BLADED WEAPON

133

SAUL LIVES

1 SAMUEL 26

ACROSS

1) KING SAUL WAS _____ ONE NIGHT, NOT AWAKE.

2) OPPOSITE OF INSIDE

3) WE HEAR WITH OUR _____.

DOWN

4) DAVID STOLE SAUL'S BOTTLE OF _____.

5) OPPOSITE OF DIE

6) VERY LONG WEAPON WITH A POINT ON THE END

7) YOU WEAR A HAT ON IT

134

SAUL DIES

I SAMUEL 31

ACROSS

1) ROYAL MEN WHO RULE OVER COUNTRIES (RHYMES WITH "SINGS")

2) SAUL'S BOYS, HIS _____, DIED IN BATTLE.

3) SAUL FELL ON HIS OWN SWORD AND _____.

DOWN

4) SAUL _____ GREATLY AGAINST GOD WHEN HE WENT TO THE FORTUNE TELLER.

5) LONG, SHARP, BLADED WEAPON

6) ISRAEL WAS DEFEATED AND _____ THE BATTLE AGAINST THE PHILISTINES.

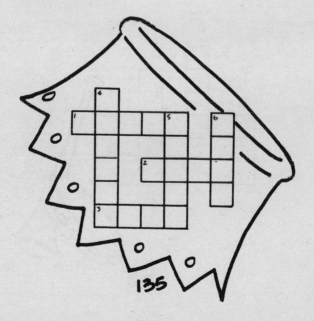

135

DAVID AND THE ARK

2 SAMUEL 6

ACROSS

1) STRONG CATTLE THAT PULLED THE WAGON

2) _____ OF THE COVENANT

3) LARGE, WHEELED CART PULLED BY OXEN

4) TEMPORARY DWELLING MADE OF HIDES OR FABRIC

DOWN

3) AN OWL ASKS, "_____?"

5) THE PEOPLE SANG A JOYFUL _____.

6) KING DAVID _____ WITH JOY (RHYMES WITH "LANCED").

7) GOD _____ HIS PROMISE.

136

DAVID'S SIN

2 SAMUEL 11

ACROSS

1) OPPOSITE OF GOOD

2) DAVID FELL IN _____ WITH BATHSHEBA.

3) OPPOSITE OF SUNRISE.

4) BATHSHEBA WAS ALREADY MARRIED TO ANOTHER _____.

DOWN

1) BEAUTIFUL MEANS FULL OF _____.

5) THE TOP OF A BUILDING

6) OPPOSITE OF OFF

7) TO BREAK GOD'S LAW - RHYMES WITH "PIN"

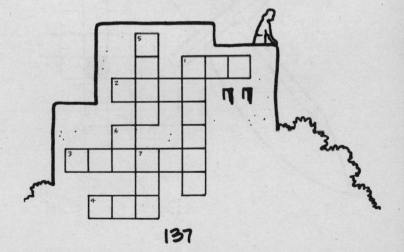

137

DAVID'S TROUBLED SONS   2 SAMUEL 13

ACROSS

1) TO TAKE A LIFE

2) DAVID STILL _____ HIS WICKED SON WITH ALL HIS HEART.

3) OPPOSITE OF SHE

4) PERIODS OF 365 DAYS — RHYMES WITH "FEARS"

DOWN

5) BAD, EVIL

6) DAVID'S SON KILLED HIS OWN _____. (RHYMES WITH "MOTHER")

7) TO WEEP

138

DAVID'S LOYAL FRIENDS

2 SAMUEL 16, 15

ACROSS

1) DAVID'S FRIENDS SAVED HIS _____.

2) ASSISTANCE - RHYMES WITH "KELP"

3) OPPOSITE OF BAD

4) PEOPLE SLEEP IN _____.

DOWN

5) PEOPLE WHO LIKE EACH OTHER ARE _____ (RHYMES WITH "ENDS").

6) OPPOSITE OF BOTTOM

7) DAVID'S FRIENDS BROUGHT _____ FOR HIM TO EAT. (RHYMES WITH "RUDE")

139

DAVID, KING AGAIN

2 SAMUEL 19

ACROSS

1) WHAT A KING WEARS ON HIS HEAD

2) HOW OLD A PERSON IS IS THEIR ____. (RHYMES WITH "PAGE")

3) NO WARS OR FIGHTING GOING ON

DOWN

4) THE SPECIAL CHAIR A KING SITS ON

5) DAVID WAS MADE ____ OVER ISRAEL AGAIN. (RHYMES WITH "SING")

6) TO CLEAN SOMETHING WITH WATER, SUCH AS, ____ DISHES

7) OPPOSITE OF HAPPY

140

YOUNG SOLOMON ANOINTED 1 KINGS 1:38-53

ACROSS

1) DAVID WAS GETTING _____, NOT YOUNG.

2) DAVID'S SON, _____, WOULD BE ISRAEL'S NEW KING.

3) ZADOK, A _____, ANOINTED SOLOMON (RHYMES WITH "LEAST").

DOWN

1) SOLOMON WAS ANOINTED WITH _____.

2) SOLOMON WAS DAVID'S _____.

4) SOLOMON RODE ON DAVID'S _____, A CROSS BETWEEN A HORSE AND A DONKEY. (RHYMES WITH "RULE")

5) SOLOMON WOULD BE THE _____ KING AFTER KING DAVID (RHYMES WITH "TEXT").

6) SOLOMON _____ ON HIS FATHER'S MULE.

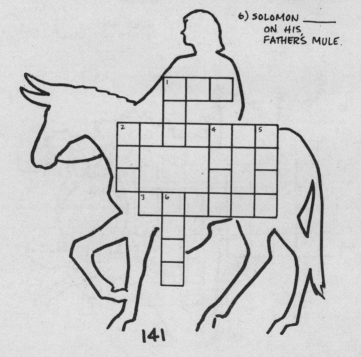

141

SOLOMON'S WISDOM

1 KINGS 3:5-15
1 KINGS 4:29-34

ACROSS

1) MUCH WEALTH

2) SOLOMON WANTED TO _____ GOD (RHYMES WITH "CURVE").

3) TO TALK TO GOD

DOWN

4) OPPOSITE OF QUESTION

5) SOLOMON WAS VERY _____. HE HAD GREAT WISDOM.

6) "_____ THY MOTHER AND THY FATHER."

7) TO QUESTION— RHYMES WITH "TASK"

142

THE TEMPLE

I KINGS 5:1-9
9:1-7

ACROSS

1) STEPS GOING UP AND DOWN

2) PEOPLE _____ UP THE TEMPLE STEPS TO GO TO WORSHIP (RHYMES WITH "TALKED")

3) THE KIND OF WOOD THEY USED TO BUILD THE TEMPLE - RHYMES WITH "FEEDER"

4) SET APART TO GOD— _____ OF HOLIES

DOWN

1) A TWINKLING LIGHT IN THE NIGHT SKY

2) LARGE, FLAT SIDES OF A ROOM OR BUILDING

5) SOLOMON BUILT THE _____.

6) THE _____ OF THE COVENANT WAS PLACED IN THE TEMPLE.

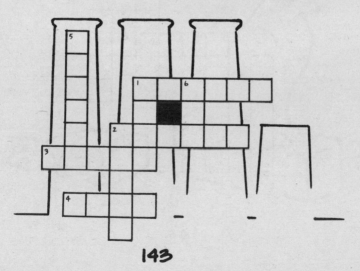

143

SOLOMON'S SINS

2 KINGS 11

ACROSS

1) KING OF EGYPT

2) FALSE GODS

3) SOLOMON MARRIED THE PHARAOH'S DAUGHTER WHO WAS FROM _____.

DOWN

1) OPPOSITE OF RICH

4) EVIL, BAD

5) SOLOMON MADE LIFE _____ (DIFFICULT) FOR THE POOR PEOPLE. (RHYMES WITH "CARD")

6) PRECIOUS YELLOW METAL

7) OPPOSITE OF DOWN

144

ELIJAH

1 KINGS 17

ACROSS

1) LARGE BLACK BIRDS LIKE CROWS - RHYMES WITH "HAVENS"

2) WATER THAT FALLS FROM THE SKY

3) ELIJAH HAD A LONG, SCRUFFY _____ GROWING FROM HIS CHIN.

DOWN

4) ELIJAH'S _____ WAS GROWN OUT LONG (RHYMES WITH "CHAIR").

5) _____ WAS A PROPHET OF GOD WITH LONG HAIR AND BEARD.

6) ELIJAH WORE CLOTHES MADE FROM ANIMAL _____, NOT CLOTH.

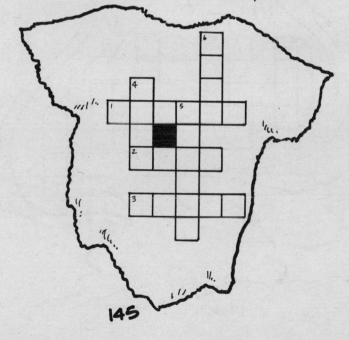

ELIJAH'S CHALLENGE

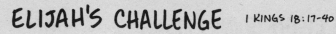

1 KINGS 18:17-40

ACROSS

1) NOT TRUE

2) HEAVY, BIG CATTLE

3) FLAMES

4) ELIJAH OFFERED HIS SACRIFICE ON AN _____.

DOWN

5) FALSE GOD

6) WATER THAT FALLS FROM THE SKY

7) GOD'S PROPHET WHO THE RAVENS FED

8) OPPOSITE OF TO

146

ELISHA JOINS ELIJAH
1 KINGS 19:19-21

ACROSS

1) BIG, STRONG CATTLE USED FOR PULLING PLOWS

2) ELISHA WAS WORKING THE _____ OF HIS FAMILY'S FARM (RHYMES WITH "SHIELDS").

3) MOTHER AND FATHER

DOWN

4) ELIJAH PUT HIS CLOAK OF ANIMAL _____ ONTO ELISHA.

5) WHERE FOOD IS GROWN "OLD MAC DONALD'S _____ "

6) OPPOSITE OF HELLO

7) _____ JOINED ELIJAH TO BE A PROPHET.

147

ELIJAH TAKEN UP INTO HEAVEN

2 KINGS 2:1-11

ACROSS

1) _____ PULL CHARIOTS.
   (RHYMES WITH "FORCES")

2) TWO-WHEELED BATTLE WAGON PULLED BY HORSES

3) FLAMES

4) MOVEMENT OF AIR – RHYMES WITH "PINNED"

DOWN

1) GOD'S DWELLING PLACE ON HIGH

5) OPPOSITE OF ON

6) OPPOSITE OF OUT

7) TO CONSUME FOOD

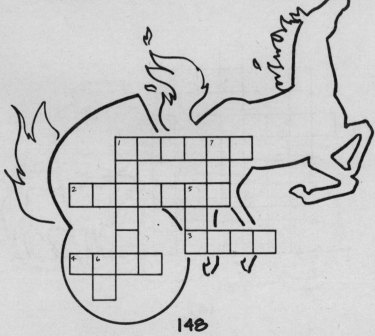

148

ELISHA AND THE OIL

2 KINGS 4:1-7

ACROSS

1) OPPOSITE OF DOWN

2) THE WIDOW COULD NOW
   ____ OFF THE DEBT
   (RHYMES WITH "HAY").

3) TALL CONTAINERS FOR
   LIQUID - RHYMES
   WITH "THROTTLES"

4) THE WIDOW _____ ALL
   OF THE JARS TO
   THEIR TOPS.

DOWN

5) LAMPS BURN ____
   FOR LIGHT

6) WE USE THIS TO
   BUY THINGS.

7) LARGE MOUTH
   CONTAINERS - RHYMES
   WITH "LOTS"

8) CONTAINERS WITH LIDS -
   RHYMES WITH "CARS"

9) " ____ AND EVERY ONE "
   RHYMES WITH "PEACH "

149

PEOPLE HEALED
FROM POISON

2 KINGS 4:38-41

ACROSS

1) OPPOSITE OF LOSE -
   RHYMES WITH "KIND"

2) A TOXIC, DEADLY
   SUBSTANCE USUALLY
   IN DRINK OR FOOD

3) TO CONSUME FOOD

DOWN

1) WE EAT _____ TO
   STAY ALIVE

2) THEY COOKED THE
   STEW IN A BIG
   _____ (RHYMES
   WITH "LOT").

4) ILL

5) OPPOSITE OF OUT

150

NAAMAN HEALED

2 KINGS 5

ACROSS

1) THE OUTER COVERING OF OUR BODIES - RHYMES WITH "SPIN"

2) TO CLEAN WITH WATER, SUCH AS _____ DISHES

3) SOMEONE WITH LEPROSY - RHYMES WITH "PEPPER"

4) THE NUMBER THAT COMES AFTER SIX

DOWN

1) A STRONG BOX TO LOCK VALUABLES IN

5) TO HAVE A DISEASE CURED

6) OPPOSITE OF FUTURE

7) _____ WAS HEALED OF HIS LEPROSY

8) A LONG, FLOWING BODY OF WATER

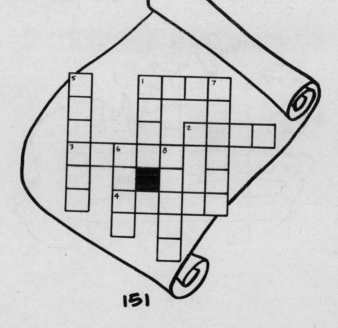

151

ELISHA AND THE
CHARIOTS OF FIRE

2 KINGS 6:8-23

ACROSS

1) WE HEAR WITH OUR _____.

2) A LARGE TOWN

3) FLAMES

4) 2-WHEELED WAR WAGONS PULLED BY SWIFT HORSES

DOWN

1) GOD SAVED THE PROPHET _____ BY SENDING FIERY CHARIOTS.

3) WE EAT _____ TO LIVE.

5) A GROUP OF SOLDIERS

6) IF YOU'RE TIRED, YOU SHOULD TAKE A _____ (RHYMES WITH "BEST")

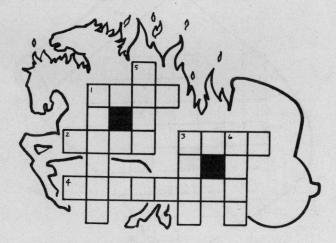

152

ELISHA DIES

2 KINGS 13:14-21

ACROSS

1) OPPOSITE OF SMALL

2) TWO-WHEELED WAR WAGON PULLED BY SWIFT HORSES

3) THE NUMBER AFTER THE NUMBER TWO

DOWN

1) _____ AND ARROW

4) A BOW SHOOTS _____.

5) TO STRIKE SOMETHING - RHYMES WITH "FIT"

6) GOD'S PROPHET WHO JOINED ELIJAH

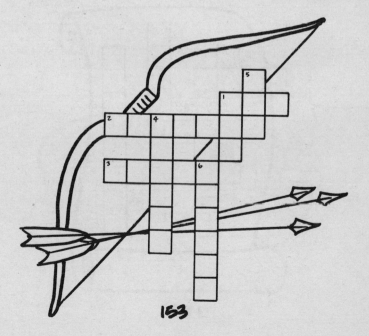

153

HEZEKIAH

2 KINGS 18

ACROSS

1) OPPOSITE OF BAD

2) A QUEEN'S HUSBAND- RHYMES WITH "RING"

3) KING HEZEKIAH WOULD ONLY _____ THE ONE TRUE GOD.

DOWN

4) OPPOSITE OF OLD

5) KING _____ LOVED GOD AND DESTROYED THE IDOLS.

6) FALSE GODS

7) MANY PAGES BOUND TOGETHER IS A _____ (RHYMES WITH "COOK").

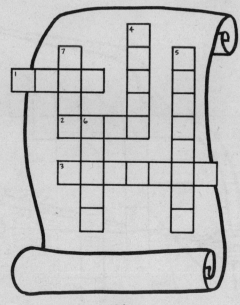

154

HEZEKIAH'S MISTAKE
2 KINGS 20:12-19

ACROSS

1) PRECIOUS WHITE METAL - FORKS AND SPOONS ARE _____WARE.

2) A PAPER SHOWING ROADS, CITIES ETC. ON IT - RHYMES WITH "TAP"

3) OPPOSITE OF POOR

4) KEPT FROM THE KNOWLEDGE OF OTHERS, UNREVEALED, HIDDEN

DOWN

1) SEASONINGS "SUGAR AND ____"

5) HARD, PROTECTIVE SUIT WORN BY SOLDIERS

6) PRECIOUS YELLOW METAL

7) RICHES, VALUABLES; "_____ CHEST" RHYMES WITH "MEASURE"

155

JOSIAH, THE YOUNG KING

2 KINGS 22

ACROSS

1) GOD SAID TO _____ HIS LAW
   (RHYMES WITH "SHEEP").
2) MANY PAGES BOUND TOGETHER
   ARE A _____.
3) PERIODS OF 365 DAYS
4) OPPOSITE OF LOST

DOWN

5) OPPOSITE OF SHE
6) HUMAN BEINGS, A
   NATION, A RACE -
   RHYMES WITH "STEEPLE"
7) OPPOSITE OF HAPPY

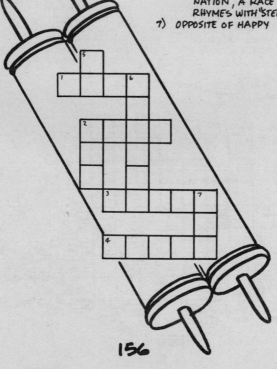

156

GOD FIGHTS FOR JEHOSHAPHAT'S ARMY

2 CHRONICLES
20:22-30

ACROSS

1) ASSISTANCE - RHYMES WITH "KELP"
2) BLACK, GOOEY SUBSTANCE USED ON ROADS - RHYMES WITH "CAR"
3) JEHOSHAPHAT PRAYED AND GOD HEARD _____ (RHYMES WITH "DIM").
4) GOD DESTROYED JUDAH'S _____ (ADVERSARY, FOE).
5) JUDAH WAS _____ BY THE LORD (RHYMES WITH "PAVED".

DOWN

6) PRIESTS CAME FROM THE TRIBE OF _____.
7) JUDAH'S ENEMIES FOUGHT EACH _____.
8) YOU MUST TAKE _____ AT A TARGET BEFORE YOU SHOOT IT.
9) A GROUP OF SOLDIERS
10) NO WAR OR FIGHTING - RHYMES WITH "NIECE"

157

KING UZZIAH

2 CHRONICLES 26:1-15

ACROSS

1) _____ BECAME KING WHEN HE WAS 16.

2) THE NUMBER THAT COMES AFTER FIFTEEN

3) TALL, NARROW BUILDINGS - RHYMES WITH "FLOWERS"

4) OPPOSITE OF MORE

5) "_____ LIKE AN EAGLE" - RHYMES WITH "POOR"

6) OPPOSITE OF FEW

DOWN

7) FARMS THAT GROW GRAPES

8) DEEP HOLES IN THE GROUND FOR WATER

9) OPPOSITE OF WEAK

10) FEMALE CHICKEN

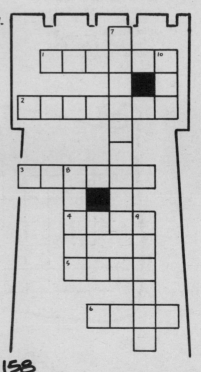

158

THE PEOPLE RETURN

EZRA 2:1 - 3:7

<u>ACROSS</u>

1) SACRIFICES WERE OFFERED ON AN _____.

2) OPPOSITE OF OVER

3) TO GO BACK TO THE PLACE YOU CAME FROM

4) THE PEOPLE SANG _____ OF JOY WHEN THEY WERE SET FREE TO GO HOME.

<u>DOWN</u>

5) OPPOSITE OF FIRST

6) BROKEN DOWN, ABANDONED CITY OR BUILDING - THE GREEK PARTHENON IS IN _____.

7) OPPOSITE OF UP

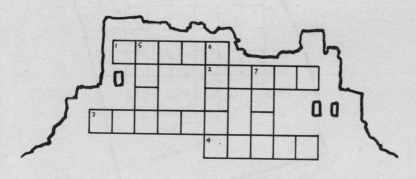

159

THE BUILDING STOPS

EZRA 4

ACROSS

1) A WRITTEN COMMUNICATION – RHYMES WITH "BETTER"

2) OPPOSITE OF START

3) AN INSTRUMENT USED TO WRITE, USES INK

DOWN

1) OPPOSITE OF FOUND

4) HOUSE OF WORSHIP

5) ONE WHO RULES – RHYMES WITH "COOLER"

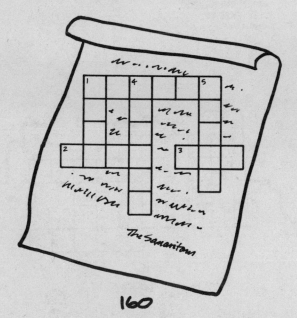

160

EZRA

EZRA 7

ACROSS

1) TO TALK, TO UTTER WORDS

2) ONE WHO SPEAKS FOR GOD

3) "_____ OF A NEEDLE"

DOWN

1) ONE WHO COPIED BOOKS AND DID THE JOB OF WRITING THINGS DOWN- RHYMES WITH " BRIBE "

4) TO GIVE INSTRUCTION, TO CAUSE TO LEARN, TO EDUCATE

5) ONLY THE _____ COULD GO INTO THE HOLY TABERNACLE

6) _____ WAS A PRIEST, PROPHET AND SCRIBE.

161

NEHEMIAH PRAYS

ACROSS

1) OPPOSITE OF ON

2) HEBREWS, CHILDREN OF
   ISRAEL - RHYMES
   WITH "NEWS"

3) OPPOSITE OF GO -
   "O ____, LET US
   ADORE HIM" -
   RHYMES WITH "SOME"

4) TALK TO GOD

DOWN

3) SMALL DRINKING
   CONTAINER - RHYMES
   WITH "PUP"

5) ____ PRAYED TO
   GOD FOR THE CITY
   OF JERUSALEM.

6) OPPOSITE OF SLOW

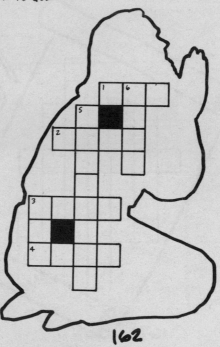

162

THE WALL FINISHED

NEHEMIAH 6:15-16

ACROSS

1) TALL, FLAT STRUCTURE SURROUNDING ANCIENT CITIES - RHYMES WITH "CALL"

2) FIX

3) OPPOSITE OF WEAK

4) OPPOSITE OF SHORT

5) THE WHOLE EARTH - RHYMES WITH "CURLED"

DOWN

1) LABOR - RHYMES WITH "PERK"

6) "COME SIT ON MY _____," SAID GRANDMA. (RHYMES WITH "CAP")

7) THE NUMBER THAT FOLLOWS FIFTY-ONE

8) MEN WHO KEEP WATCH OVER SOMEONE OR SOMETHING (RHYMES WITH "YARDS")

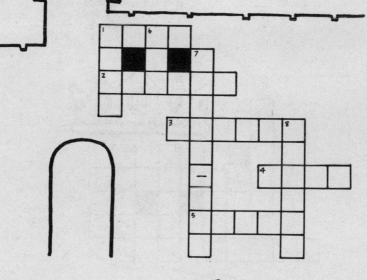

163

ESTHER
BECOMES
QUEEN

ESTHER 2:1-8

ACROSS

1) OPPOSITE OF OFF

2) FULL OF BEAUTY

3) THE KING OF PERSIA CHOSE _____ TO BE HIS QUEEN.

4) QUEEN ESTHER WORE A ROYAL _____ ON HER HEAD.

DOWN

5) THE KING _____ ESTHER MORE THAN ANY OTHER WOMAN.

6) A KING'S WIFE IS A _____.

7) PRESENTS

8) ONE WHO RULES - A STICK FOR MEASURING

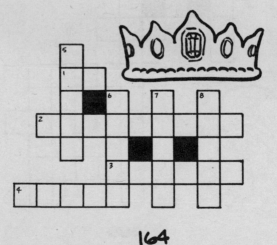

164

MORDECAI
HONORED

ESTHER 6:1-11

ACROSS

1) THE KING OF PERSIA
   HONORED _____ .

2) RESPECT,
   "_____ THY MOTHER
   AND THY FATHER "

3) LARGE, SWIFT ANIMAL
   FOR RIDING - RHYMES
   WITH "COURSE"

DOWN

1) OPPOSITE OF WOMAN

4) OPPOSITE OF COMMON -
   RHYMES WITH "CARE"

5) A KING WEARS ONE
   ON HIS HEAD

6) A MAN ____ ON A
   HORSE TO RIDE IT
   (RHYMES WITH
   "FITS").

165

JOB

JOB

ACROSS

1) OPPOSITE OF RICH

2) HAVING PAIN OR DISTRESS

3) OPPOSITE OF SHE

4) JOB SERVED THE LORD. HE LOVED _____.

DOWN

1) HURT- RHYMES WITH "RAIN"

5) A LOT- RHYMES WITH "SUCH"

6) JOB _____ GOD WITH ALL HIS HEART.

7) GOD TOOK EVERYTHING AWAY FROM HIS SERVANT _____.

8) OPPOSITE OF OUT

9) OPPOSITE OF BAD- JOB WAS A _____ MAN.

166

PSALM 23

ACROSS

1) " I WILL FEAR
      NO _____ "

2) " I WILL DWELL IN THE
      HOUSE OF THE
      LORD _____ "

3) " HE MAKES ME LIE
      DOWN IN _____
      PASTURES "

4) " THE _____ IS MY
      SHEPHERD "

DOWN

3) TO GET BIGGER

5) " THOUGH I WALK
      THROUGH THE _____
      OF THE SHADOW
      OF DEATH "

6) " THE LORD IS MY _____ "

7) " HE LEADS ME BESIDE
      THE _____ WATERS "

8) " SURELY GOODNESS AND
      MERCY SHALL
      FOLLOW ___ "

167

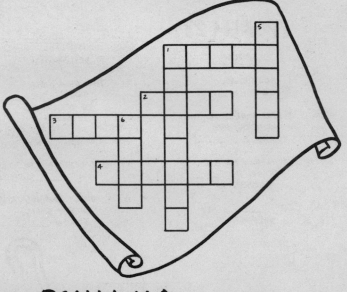

PSALM 100

ACROSS

1) OPPOSITE OF LIE

2) GOD HAS _____ US AND NOT WE OURSELVES (RHYMES WITH "PAID")

3) SING A _____ OF PRAISE

4) FULL OF JOY

DOWN

1) FULL OF THANKS

5) WOOLY CREATURES THAT NEED A SHEPHERD

6) GOD IS _____ (OPPOSITE OF BAD).

168

PSALM 148

ACROSS

1) "LIGHT HOLDER" OF THE NIGHT SKY

2) SMALL, TWINKLING LIGHTS OF THE NIGHT SKY

3) HUMAN BEINGS, NATION, RACE - RHYMES WITH "STEEPLE"

4) SMALL MOUNTAINS

5) "LIGHT HOLDER" OF THE DAY

6) _____ CREATED EVERYTHING, PRAISE HIM!

DOWN

7) GOD'S MESSENGERS

8) TALL PLANTS WITH TRUNKS - RHYMES WITH "SEAS"

9) WORSHIP, ADORE, EXTOL - RHYMES WITH "RAISE"

10) OPPOSITE OF WOMEN

11) MEN WHO RULE OVER COUNTRIES - RHYMES WITH "RINGS"

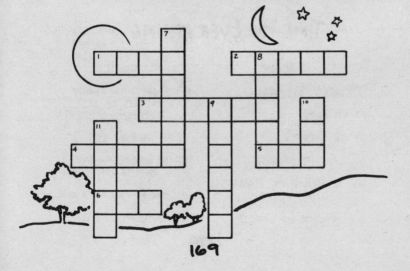

169

A Time For Everything

Ecclesiastes 3:1-8

ACROSS

1) CLOCKS TELL _____.

2) TO CURE

3) TO WEEP

4) OPPOSITE OF HATE

5) TO CONSTRUCT - RHYMES WITH "FILLED"

6) OPPOSITE OF LOVE

DOWN

4) SOMETHING FUNNY MAKES US _____. (OPPOSITE OF CRY)

7) TO TAKE A LIFE

8) NO WAR OR FIGHTING - RHYMES WITH "NIECE"

9) THE NUMBER AFTER ONE

10) OPPOSITE OF LIVE

170

ISAIAH'S PROPHESY OF JESUS

ISAIAH 9:6

ACROSS

1) COMING INTO THE WORLD -
   RHYMES WITH "HORN"

2) ONE WHO COUNSELS

3) OPPOSITE OF LOST

4) VERY YOUNG PERSON,
   AN OFFSPRING -
   RHYMES WITH
   "WILD"

DOWN

5) MARVELOUS, FULL
   OF WONDER

6) OPPOSITE OF DAUGHTER,
   "___ OF GOD"

7) JESUS, THE SON
   OF ___

8) THE SON OF A KING -
   RHYMES WITH "SINCE"

171

JEREMIAH'S VISION

JEREMIAH 24

ACROSS

1) NO WAR OR FIGHTING

2) OPPOSITE OF GOOD

3) SWEET FRUITS OF THE FIG TREE

4) A WRITTEN COMMUNICATION - RHYMES WITH "BETTER"

5) OPPOSITE OF PUSH

DOWN

1) TALK TO GOD

6) PRISONER, HOSTAGE, HELD AGAINST THEIR WILL

7) OPPOSITE OF NONE

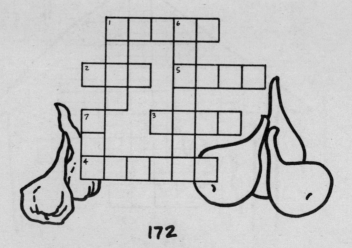

172

ISRAEL IN BABYLON

JEREMIAH 39:1-10
EZEKIEL 37

ACROSS

1) THE CHILDREN OF _____ WERE TAKEN AWAY TO BABYLON.

2) THE JEWS WOULD BE CAPTIVES FOR SEVENTY _____ (RHYMES WITH "TEARS")

3) TO CONSUME WITH FIRE- RHYMES WITH "TURN"

DOWN

4) A LARGE TOWN

5) THE JEWS WERE TAKEN TO _____.

6) BABYLON WAS A LAND FAR _____.

7) THE CHILDREN OF ISRAEL WOULD _____ SONGS TO REMEMBER THEIR HOMELAND.

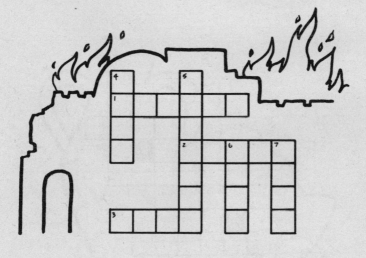

173

YOUNG DANIEL

DANIEL 1:1-7

ACROSS

1) A SWEET, PURPLE FRUIT - RHYMES WITH "DRUM"

2) A MAN WHO RULES OVER A COUNTRY

3) OPPOSITE OF IN

7) YOUNG _____ WOULD ONLY EAT THE FOOD OF HIS PEOPLE.

DOWN

1) A SON OF A KING

4) OPPOSITE OF OLD

5) DANIEL WOULD NOT EAT THE KING'S _____.

6) THE NUMBER THAT COMES BEFORE ELEVEN

174

THE FIERY FURNACE

DANIEL 3:19-30

ACROSS

1) TO BE BOUND WITH ROPE - RHYMES WITH "LIED"

2) THICK, LONG CORDS FOR TYING - RHYMES WITH "HOPES"

3) THE NUMBER AFTER THE NUMBER TWO

DOWN

4) KING NEBUCHADNEZZAR WORSHIPED THE ONE TRUE ___ AFTER HE SAW THE MEN COME OUT OF THE FIRE. (OPPOSITE OF FALSE)

5) FLAMES

6) CONSUMED BY FIRE - RHYMES WITH "TURNED"

7) ONE MORE THAN THREE

8) OPPOSITE OF COLD

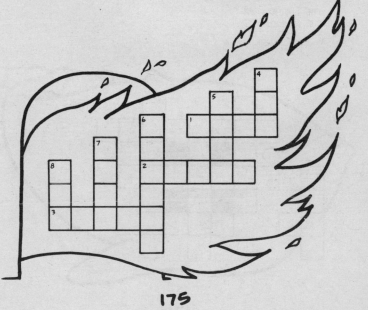

175

JONAH
AND THE CITY OF NINEVEH

ACROSS

1) VERY LARGE BODY OF WATER - RHYMES WITH "BEE"

2) FINNED CREATURES OF THE WATER - RHYMES WITH "DISH"

3) TO TAKE FOOD DOWN THE THROAT INTO THE STOMACH - RHYMES WITH "HOLLOW"

4) OPPOSITE OF OUT

5) THE LIQUID THAT FISH SWIM IN

DOWN

3) A LARGE, SEAGOING VESSEL - RHYMES WITH "SLIP"

6) STOMACH - RHYMES WITH "JELLY"

7) JONAH DID NOT WANT TO GO TO THE CITY OF _____ .

8) _____ WAS SWALLOWED BY A GREAT FISH.

176

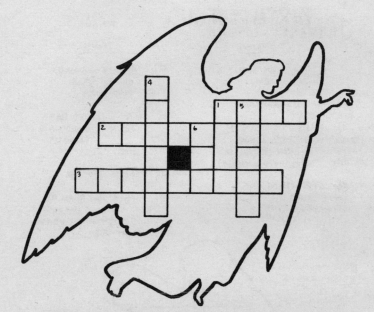

GABRIEL VISITS MARY
LUKE 1:26-38

ACROSS

1) GABRIEL TOLD _____ SHE WOULD BEAR A SON AND CALL HIM JESUS.

2) _____ WOULD BE THE SAVIOR OF THE WORLD.

3) JOSEPH WAS A _____ WHO WORKED WITH WOOD.

DOWN

4) MARY WAS TO BE MARRIED TO _____.

5) A MESSENGER OF GOD, GABRIEL WAS AN _____.

6) OPPOSITE OF DAUGHTER

177

BIRTH OF JESUS

LUKE 2:1-7

ACROSS

1) _____ WAS BORN IN BETHLEHEM.

2) MARY'S HUSBAND

3) MARY PUT JESUS IN A _____ FOR A CRIB (RHYMES WITH "STRANGER").

4) OPPOSITE OF SHE

DOWN

5) THE CITY OF DAVID, WHERE JESUS WAS BORN

6) MARY WRAPPED BABY JESUS IN SWADDLING _____. (RHYMES WITH "ROSE")

7) JESUS' MOTHER

8) JESUS WAS BORN IN A STABLE BECAUSE THERE WAS NO ROOM AT THE _____.

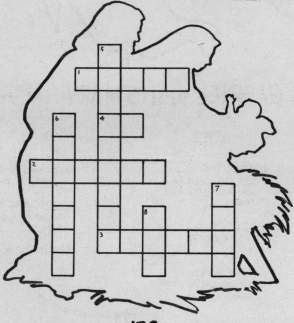

178

JESUS PRESENTED AT TEMPLE

LUKE 22:21-38

ACROSS

1) HOUSE OF WORSHIP

2) PEACEFUL BIRDS - RHYMES WITH "LOVES"

3) THE NUMBER AFTER THIRTY-NINE

DOWN

4) MARY AND JOSEPH BROUGHT BABY _____ TO THE TEMPLE.

5) FATHER, SON, HOLY _____

6) JESUS IS THE _____ OF THE WORLD (ONE WHO SAVES).

7) THE NUMBER THAT COMES AFTER NUMBER ONE

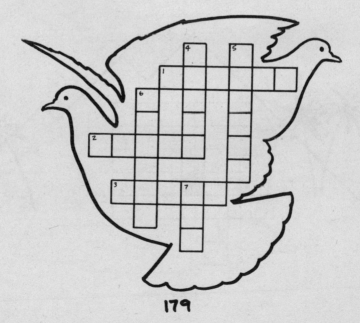

179

FLIGHT INTO EGYPT

MATTHEW 2:13-18

ACROSS

1) MARY'S HUSBAND

2) VERY YOUNG CHILD -
   RHYMES WITH "MAYBE"

3) SCHEME OR PLAN -
   RHYMES WITH "CLOT"

4) OPPOSITE OF DAY

DOWN

5) THE LAND WHERE
   PHARAOHS ONCE RULED,
   HOME OF THE PYRAMIDS

6) KING _____ SOUGHT
   TO DESTROY BABY
   JESUS.

7) A MESSENGER OF GOD

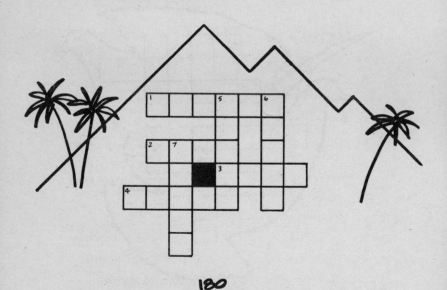

JESUS IN THE TEMPLE

LUKE 2:41-53

ACROSS

1) ONES WHO TEACH, INSTRUCTORS

2) HOUSE OF WORSHIP

3) OPPOSITE OF QUESTIONS

10) MOTHER OF JESUS

DOWN

4) JESUS WAS _____ YEARS OLD (THE NUMBER AFTER ELEVEN)

5) AS A BOY, _____ AMAZED THE TEACHERS IN THE TEMPLE.

6) TO SET UP A TEMPORARY LODGING PLACE - RHYMES WITH "LAMP"

7) ANXIETY, CONCERN, FRET - RHYMES WITH "HURRY"

8) OPPOSITE OF NIGHTS

9) MARY'S HUSBAND

181

JESUS IS BAPTIZED

LUKE 3:21-22

ACROSS

1) _____ THE BAPTIST BAPTIZED JESUS.

2) A BIRD WHICH SYMBOLIZES THE HOLY SPIRIT, PEACE

3) A LONG, FLOWING BODY OF WATER - RHYMES WITH "SLIVER"

4) FATHER, SON, HOLY _____

DOWN

5) OPPOSITE OF OUT

6) "THIS IS MY BELOVED _____ IN WHOM I AM WELL PLEASED" SAID GOD.

7) THEY HEARD GOD'S _____ FROM HEAVEN (RHYMES WITH "CHOICE").

1) THE SON OF GOD

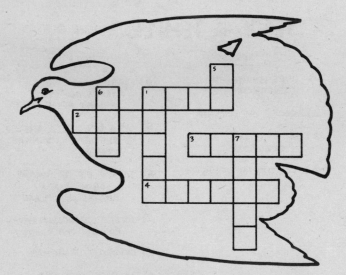

182

ANDREW AND JOHN   JOHN 1:35-39

ACROSS

1) TO GO AFTER SOMEONE - RHYMES WITH "HOLLOW"

2) A BABY SHEEP

3) SIMON PETER'S BROTHER, ONE OF CHRIST'S FIRST FOLLOWERS

DOWN

4) AUTHOR OF THE FOURTH GOSPEL IN THE NEW TESTAMENT, BROTHER OF JAMES

5) SPOKE, UTTERED SPEECH - RHYMES WITH "WALKED"

6) ANOTHER WORD FOR "I", JESUS SAID, "FOLLOW ___."

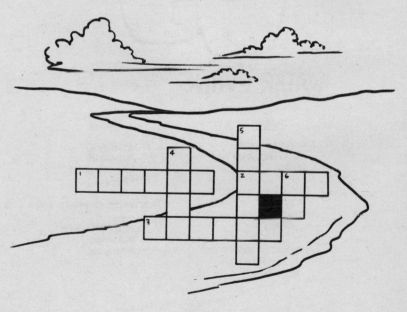

183

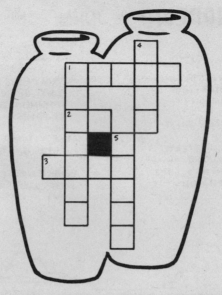

WATER to WINE

JOHN 2:1-11

ACROSS

1) COLORLESS LIQUID IN RIVERS AND SEAS

2) THE BRIDE SAID, "I ___." (OPPOSITE OF DON'T)

3) FERMENTED GRAPE JUICE - RHYMES WITH "FINE"

DOWN

1) A MARRIAGE CEREMONY - RHYMES WITH "BEDDING"

4) OPPOSITE OF WORST

5) _____ CHANGED THE WATER INTO WINE.

NICODEMUS

JOHN 3: 1-21

ACROSS

1) TO COME INTO THIS WORLD - RHYMES WITH "HORN"

2) ANGRY

3) WE ARE BAPTIZED IN _____ (A CLEAR LIQUID).

4) FATHER, SON, HOLY _____

DOWN

1) A BASEBALL IS HIT WITH A _____.

5) MORE THAN ONCE - "YOU MUST BE BORN _____."

6) JESUS TOLD _____ THAT HE MUST BE BORN AGAIN.

7) OPPOSITE OF DEATH

2) OPPOSITE OF WOMAN

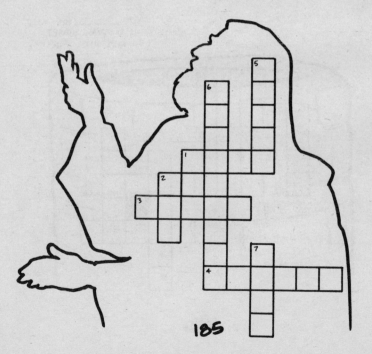

185

THE WOMAN AT THE WELL

JOHN 4:5-30

ACROSS

1) OPPOSITE OF MAN

2) ONE WHO SPEAKS FOR GOD

3) TO CONSUME A LIQUID - RHYMES WITH "THINK"

DOWN

1) A DEEP HOLE FROM WHICH WATER IS DRAWN - RHYMES WITH "FELL"

4) _____ COMES OUT OF A SPRING.

5) MANY TIMES, FREQUENTLY - RHYMES WITH "SOFTEN"

6) IF YOU _____, YOU SHOULD DRINK WATER (RHYMES WITH "FIRST").

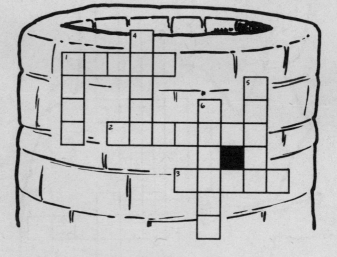

186

THE CITY OF NAZARETH REJECTS JESUS

LUKE 4:16-30

ACROSS

1) JESUS GREW UP IN THE CITY OF
   _____.

2) JESUS LIVED THERE AS A _____
   (OPPOSITE OF GIRL).

3) A LARGE TOWN - RHYMES WITH "PITY"

DOWN

4) THE LORD'S DAY, DAY OF REST

5) OPPOSITE OF IN

6) MAD, FULL OF ANGER

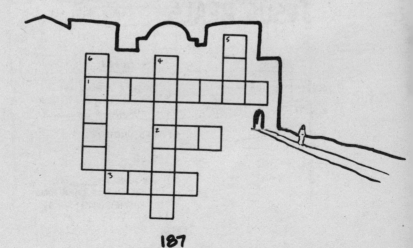

187

JESUS HEALS

LUKE 4:33-42

ACROSS

1) OPPOSITE OF HIM

2) CURED

3) FATHER, SON,
   HOLY _____

DOWN

4) WHEN A PERSON IS
   HOT FROM AN ILLNESS,
   HE HAS A _____.

5) BAD, WICKED

6) SICK

7) WE HAVE A _____ AT
   THE END OF EACH ARM —
   RHYMES WITH "SAND"

188

THE POOL OF BETHESDA

JOHN 5:1-16

<u>ACROSS</u>

1) OPPOSITE OF DOWN

2) OPPOSITE OF OUT OF

3) STROLLED, TRAVELED BY FOOT - RHYMES WITH "TALKED"

4) CURVED STRUCTURE ON A BUILDING - RHYMES WITH "PARCH"

<u>DOWN</u>

3) LABOR, EFFORT

5) POND, SMALL BODY OF WATER - RHYMES WITH "COOL"

6) ILLNESS, SICKNESS, AILMENT

189

JESUS CALLS MATTHEW MARK 2:13-14

ACROSS

1) WE USE THIS TO BUY THINGS

2) MONEY COLLECTED FROM THE PEOPLE BY THE GOVERNMENT - RHYMES WITH "FACTS"

3) HUMAN BEINGS, RACE, NATION - RHYMES WITH "STEEPLE"

DOWN

1) JESUS CALLED _____, THE TAX COLLECTOR, TO BE ONE OF HIS DESCIPLES.

4) ANOTHER WORD FOR "I" - JESUS SAID, "FOLLOW ___."

5) TO GO AFTER SOMEONE, "_____ THE LEADER" - RHYMES WITH "HOLLOW"

190

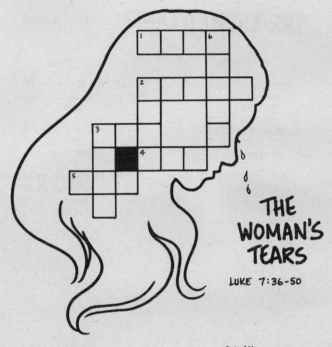

THE WOMAN'S TEARS

LUKE 7:36-50

ACROSS

1) THE WOMAN WASHED JESUS' _____ WITH HER TEARS.

2) OPPOSITE OF MAN (FEMALE)

3) OPPOSITE OF HERS

4) JESUS FORGAVE _____ SINS (OPPOSITE OF HIS).

5) TO BREAK GOD'S LAW

DOWN

2) TO CLEAN SOMETHING WITH WATER – _____ DISHES

3) LONG STRANDS THAT GROW ON OUR HEADS. RHYMES WITH "FAIR"

6) _____ COME FROM OUR EYES WHEN WE CRY.

191

THE LIGHTED LAMP

LUKE 8:16-18

ACROSS

1) THE WHOLE EARTH —
   RHYMES WITH
   "CURLED"

2) OPPOSITE OF DARK

3) WE SLEEP IN A _____.

DOWN

2) YOU BURN OIL IN
   A _____ FOR
   LIGHT

4) OPPOSITE OF OVER

5) OPPOSITE OF IN

6) TO CONCEAL SOMETHING,
   KEEP IT SECRET —
   RHYMES WITH
   "SIDE"

192

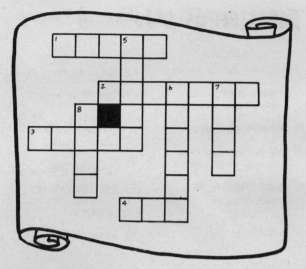

THE WOMAN
IN THE CROWD

MARK 5:22-34

ACROSS

1) TO MAKE PHYSICAL CONTACT - THE WOMAN REACHED TO _____ JESUS' ROBE (RHYMES WITH "MUCH").

2) PHYSICIANS

3) _____ RUNS THROUGH OUR VEINS

4) OPPOSITE OF HE

DOWN

5) A LARGE GROUP OF PEOPLE - RHYMES WITH "LOUD"

6) THE NUMBER AFTER ELEVEN

7) A LONG, FLOWING GARMENT - RHYMES WITH "LOBE"

8) OPPOSITE OF RICH

193

JESUS FEEDS THOUSANDS
MATTHEW 14:15-21

ACROSS

1) A WOVEN CONTAINER

2) FINNED CREATURES OF THE WATER

3) OPPOSITE OF EMPTY

4) THE BOY BROUGHT FIVE _____ OF BREAD.

5) PARTS, FRAGMENTS - RHYMES WITH "NIECES"

10) OPPOSITE OF GIRL

DOWN

2) ONE MORE THAN FOUR

4) OPPOSITE OF EARLY

6) JESUS FED _____ OF THE PEOPLE, EVERY SINGLE ONE.

7) ONE PLUS ONE

8) THE PEOPLE WERE _____ BEFORE THEY HAD EATEN.

9) OPPOSITE OF DOWN

194

PETER ON THE WATER

Matthew 14:28-31

ACROSS

1) JESUS SAID TO PETER, "_____".
   (RHYMES WITH "SOME")

2) OPPOSITE OF FLOAT

3) FULL OF FEAR

4) ANOTHER WORD FOR "I" -
   RHYMES WITH "BE"

DOWN

5) TO STROLL OR
   TRAVEL BY FOOT

6) _____ TRIED TO WALK
   ON WATER
   WITH JESUS.

7) MOVEMENT OF THE AIR-
   RHYMES WITH "SINNED"

8) TO RESCUE- RHYMES
   WITH "CAVE"

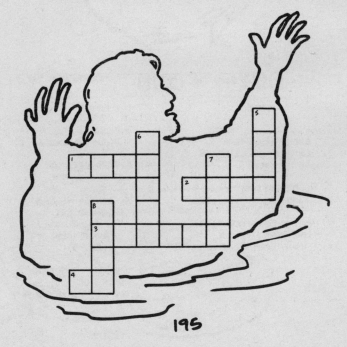

195

THE FISH AND THE COIN   MATTHEW 17:24-27

ACROSS

1) YOU USE A _____ ON THE END OF A LINE TO CATCH A FISH (RHYMES WITH "BOOK").

2) PEOPLE YOU DON'T KNOW - RHYMES WITH "RANGERS"

3) MONEY COLLECTED FROM THE PEOPLE BY THE GOVERNMENT - RHYMES WITH "SACKS"

DOWN

4) A ROUND, METAL PIECE OF MONEY

5) FINNED CREATURE OF THE WATER

6) YOU MIX WHITE AND BLACK TO GET THE COLOR _____ (RHYMES WITH "TRAY")

7) YOU EAT AND SPEAK WITH YOUR _____ (RHYMES WITH "SOUTH").

196

Answer Pages

1

TRAVEL THE PATH THAT MAKES A SENTENCE.

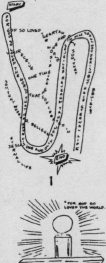

2

AFTER GOING THROUGH THE MAZE ON THE PREVIOUS PAGE, FILL IN THE BLANKS BELOW TO FINISH THE SENTENCE.

"FOR GOD SO LOVED THE WORLD THAT HE GAVE HIS ONE AND ONLY SON, THAT WHOEVER BELIEVES IN HIM SHALL NOT PERISH BUT HAVE ETERNAL LIFE."

JOHN 3:16

3

FIND THE WORDS BELOW IN THE WORDSEARCH PUZZLE.

```
J R U A M D C I W A U I H X
M G O T P N S C S M L E I T
I O F B F T L O V E D Y M G
E O R K T B J F C V T G H K
Q L Q U S E H G P R N I P L
E A R B E L I E V E S O M T
C H R X N B V C O G K O L Q
L N O R L D A S U P U P B W
W R Q G U H O A M V K L X I
J N B S D T Y H P W A I C Z
P K L Y V L O O U Y I T F O
Z P E R I S H B N V T E K V
H F I J G F V X H C W B H F
P E T E R N A L T O B G Q J
O N R J G 2 M E X V N V R Z
```

ETERNAL	HIM
WORLD	LIFE
SON	BELIEVES
PERISH	HIS
GOD	LOVED

4

"FOR GOD SO LOVED THE WORLD...."

FINISH THE PICTURE.

5

FIND THE WORDS TO THIS VERSE IN THE WORDSEARCH BELOW.

"FOR ALL HAVE SINNED AND FALL SHORT OF THE GLORY OF GOD."

ROMANS 3:23

```
R S H U K T E E B F N M T S
C I X M A Q S H O R T U C H
G E L Q P U V R F E S V O G
T X G L O R Y D R F S M A
D Q P B S L K Z F V C I Z H
I M A W 3 B T W X E G N L U
N J D K M G O A H L N W V
O P I B W N F O R U K E R F
W A E M J O O N S O B O G R
H Y P B T U U N V J P L C D
O M Q V Y P F A T H E G R S
E L V A X B J C N F Z Q U T
N P B H N B H X K S L R R
F V A F S O O E J Z B Q T
N C Z L U R Q X O U F O H G I
Y G O D H D A E D R V U C F
```

6

FIND THE WORDS TO THIS VERSE IN THE WORDSEARCH BELOW.

"...WHILE WE WERE STILL SINNERS CHRIST DIED FOR US."

ROMANS 5:8b

```
K C E D M T W T S F E C J Y
H T C A P H V A D X P J H U
P S U S E Q R D R W E Z C S
A T P G S N G J S E L O E
G I V I T B A Y B A R G Y
M L S X W H I L E S S Z E J
M U W G O S B N I R U D E N
V E I B L K C Q E M Q D
I N H W M M Q U O A R J U B
L Q E Z D V N S T Y H C R J
F K G O O X D I R U E P P L
Q R X E X X E U H B R B S P
T L J E C Q U U O L D W V T K
H Y N Z D M U K S I N E L X
```

7

USE THE CODE CHART TO MATCH THE NUMBERS WITH LETTERS. USE THE COLUMN GOING DOWN, FIRST, THEN WRITE THE LETTERS IN THE BLANKS.

	1	2	3	4	5	6
1	A	F	K	P	U	Z
2	B	G	L	Q	V	
3	C	H	M	R	W	
4	D	I	N	S	X	
5	E	J	O	T	Y	

"FOR THE WAGES OF
SIN IS DEATH, BUT
THE GIFT OF GOD
IS ETERNAL LIFE
IN CHRIST JESUS
OUR LORD."

ROMANS 6:23

8

CONNECT-THE-DOTS

9

TRAVEL THE PATH THAT MAKES A SENTENCE.

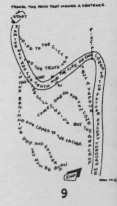

JOHN 14:6

10

AFTER GOING THROUGH THE MAZE ON THE PREVIOUS PAGE, FILL IN THE BLANKS BELOW TO FINISH THE SENTENCE.

"I AM THE WAY AND THE
TRUTH AND THE LIFE.
NO ONE COMES TO
THE FATHER EXCEPT
THROUGH ME."

JOHN 14:6

NOW FIND THE UNDERLINED WORDS IN THE WORDSEARCH BELOW.

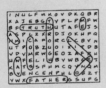

11

USE THE CODE CHART TO MATCH THE NUMBERS WITH LETTERS. USE THE COLUMN GOING DOWN, FIRST, THEN WRITE THE LETTERS IN THE BLANKS.

	1	2	3	4	5	6
1	A	F	K	P	U	Z
2	B	G	L	Q	V	
3	C	H	M	R	W	
4	D	I	N	S	X	
5	E	J	O	T	Y	

JOHN 5:24

"I TELL YOU THE
TRUTH, WHOEVER
HEARS MY WORD
AND BELIEVES
HIM WHO SENT ME
HAS ETERNAL
LIFE AND WILL NOT
BE CONDEMNED..."

12

FINISH THE PICTURE OF JESUS.

13

TRAVEL THE PATH THAT MAKES A SENTENCE.

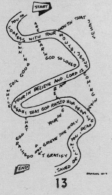

ROMANS 10:9

14

AFTER GOING THROUGH THE MAZE ON THE PREVIOUS PAGE, FILL IN THE BLANKS BELOW TO FINISH THE SENTENCE.

"IF YOU CONFESS
WITH YOUR MOUTH,
'JESUS IS LORD,' AND
BELIEVE IN YOUR
HEART THAT GOD
RAISED HIM FROM
THE DEAD, YOU WILL BE
SAVED."

ROMANS 10:9

15

FIND THE WORDS BELOW IN THE WORDSEARCH PUZZLE.

LORD   RAISED
HEART   MOUTH
DEAD   BELIEVE
CONFESS   JESUS
SAVED

COLOR THE PICTURE.

16

JESUS IS KNOCKING AT THE DOOR OF YOUR HEART. WHAT SHOULD YOU DO?

USE THE CODE CHART BELOW TO MATCH THE CODES WITH LETTERS. USE THE COLUMN GOING DOWN FIRST, THEN WRITE THE LETTERS IN THE BLANKS TO COMPLETE THE VERSE.
THEN YOU WILL KNOW WHAT TO DO!

	1	2	3	4	5	6	7
1	A	H	I	P	Q	X	Y
2	B	G	J	O	R	W	Z
3	C	F	K	N	S	V	
4	D	E	L	M	T	U	

"HERE I AM! I STAND
AT THE DOOR AND
KNOCK."

CONTINUED NEXT PAGE...

17

CONTINUED FROM PREVIOUS PAGE.

	1	2	3	4	5	6	7
1	A	H	I	P	Q	X	Y
2	B	G	J	O	R	W	Z
3	C	F	K	N	S	V	
4	D	E	L	M	T	U	

"IF ANYONE HEARS
MY VOICE AND
OPENS THE DOOR,
I WILL COME IN
AND EAT WITH
HIM, AND HE WITH
ME."

REVELATION 3:20

18

19

DO YOU KNOW JESUS LOVES YOU? DO YOU KNOW HOW MUCH JESUS LOVES YOU? HE LOVES YOU SO MUCH THAT HE DIED TO PAY THE PRICE FOR YOUR SIN. THERE IS ONLY ONE SIN THAT GOD WILL NOT FORGIVE. THAT SIN IS NOT BELIEVING IN JESUS AND WHAT HE DID FOR YOU AND ALL OF US. WITHOUT JESUS, WITHOUT ACCEPTING THAT HE DIED FOR US, NO ONE CAN GO TO HEAVEN.

THREE DAYS AFTER JESUS DIED, HE WAS RAISED TO NEW LIFE. HE WANTS TO SHARE THAT WITH US TOO! HE WANTS TO GIVE US NEW LIFE ... ETERNAL LIFE?

DO YOU WANT TO ASK JESUS TO COME INTO YOUR HEART AND YOUR LIFE? ALL YOU NEED TO DO IS ASK HIM. YOU COULD SAY A PRAYER LIKE THIS:

DEAR JESUS,

I KNOW I AM A SINNER AND THAT YOU DIED FOR ALL MY SINS. I KNOW YOU ROSE FROM THE DEAD. JESUS, I ASK YOU NOW TO COME INTO MY HEART AND TAKE CONTROL OF MY LIFE.
THANK YOU FOR ALL YOU HAVE DONE FOR ME.
TEACH ME YOUR WAYS, JESUS, AND HELP ME TO GROW UP WITH YOU.

IN JESUS' NAME, I PRAY. AMEN.

IF YOU HAVE NEVER INVITED JESUS INTO YOUR HEART AND LIFE BUT YOU WANT TO NOW, GO TO THE NEXT PAGE AND WRITE OUT YOUR PRAYER IN YOUR OWN WORDS. JUST TELL JESUS HOW YOU REALLY FEEL.

20

MY VERY OWN PRAYER TO INVITE JESUS INTO MY HEART AND LIFE.

DATE: _____

DEAR LORD JESUS,

_____
_____
_____
_____
_____
_____
_____
_____

IN JESUS' NAME, AMEN.

_____
YOUR NAME

21

IF YOU INVITE JESUS INTO YOUR HEART?
FIND YOUR WAY TO JESUS:

22

WOW! IF YOU ASKED JESUS INTO YOUR LIFE, YOU ARE NOW A CHRISTIAN! YOU ARE NOW A CHILD OF GOD!

LET'S LEARN HOW TO GET TO KNOW JESUS BETTER.

UNSCRAMBLE THE WORDS BELOW TO FIND OUT HOW TO BEGIN.

1.) TO BECOME A CHILD OF GOD, YOU HAD TO ASK JESUS INTO YOUR HEART. THIS IS CALLED PRAYING.
IYGNRAP

2) PRAYING IS TALKING WITH GOD.
GTINALK

3) JUST LIKE YOU TALK WITH YOUR MOM OR DAD, GOD WANTS YOU TO TALK WITH HIM.
TWNAS   KTLA

4) IT DOES NOT STOP THERE. GOD WANTS TO TALK TO YOU! JESUS SPEAKS TO YOU THROUGH HIS WORD.
DRWO

5) THE ONLY WAY TO REALLY KNOW JESUS IS TO READ ABOUT HIM.
ARDE   IHM

6) YOU READ ABOUT JESUS IN THE HOLY BIBLE.
EBLIB   JSSUE

23

IN THE FOLLOWING WORDSEARCH PUZZLE, FIND AND CIRCLE THE WORDS LISTED.

THEY CAN BE FOUND IN LINES GOING FORWARD, BACKWARD, UP, DOWN, OR DIAGONALLY.

```
O F C L P Y Y R F H E Y O G
O X G R A E H Y D R I S M A
O Q P B S L K Z F V G H Z H
B M B W J B E A T H G N L V
N J D K M H O O A H L N W O
O F I B O N F O U K R P I
W A E V O Q D N S R D G C
O O K C K U W V J A L C E
Q A Q Y V P F A T P B T S
V L E A L E D E V O L G S T
```

LOVED	HEARS	EAT
KNOCK	VOICE	ANYONE
DOOR	HIM	STAND

24

25

WHAT HAVE YOU LEARNED ABOUT BEING A CHILD OF GOD?

FIND AND CIRCLE THE WORDS LISTED BELOW.

```
T X I G O O R Y D R F S M A
D Q B P S L K Z F V C I K H
I W O N J B T W Y R G N L U
N W O K M 6 O O U A L N A W
B F I B W N G O D U R K T F
W I E M J B I B L E B D G R
W H N P B T W W V J D L C D
O V Q V Q Y A R P A O H A G R S
H I N G L B I G U S E D L T
N T H S N I B H X K R L K R
R E F A S D O S E A I B Q T
N C Z L L U Q X O U F D H G J
I G O O U D A E D K V U C P
```

PRAY   WORD   TALK

READ   JESUS   GOD

BIBLE   SAVIOUR   INVITE

26

CONNECT THE DOTS
AND FINISH THE PHRASE.

JESUS, THE L I O N OF JUDAH!

27

ACROSS

1. GOD _GAVE_ US HIS ONE AND ONLY SO

2. NOW WE CAN HAVE ETERNAL _LIFE_ .

3. JESUS KNOCKS AT THE DOORS OF OUR _HEARTS_

4. IF WE HAVE _INVITED_ HIM IN, HE WILL NEVER LEAVE US .

DOWN

5. WE ARE NOW A CHILD OF _GOD_ .

6. WE TALK TO HIM BY _PRAYING_ .

7. HE TALKS TO US THROUGH _HIS_ WORD.

8. HIS WORD IS THE _BIBLE_ .

WORD LIST

PRAYING	HEARTS
LIFE	BIBLE
GAVE	HIS
INVITED	GOD

28

29

SOMETIMES, IT'S NOT EASY TO READ THE BIBLE EVERY DAY. OTHER THINGS WILL TRY TO GET IN THE WAY, BUT IF YOU REALLY WANT TO GROW AS A CHRISTIAN, IT IS BEST TO READ IN GOD'S WORD EACH DAY.

FIND YOUR WAY TO THE BIBLE

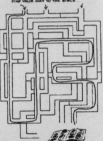

30

TRAVEL THE PATH THAT MAKES A SENTENCE

31

AFTER GOING THROUGH THE MAZE ON THE PREVIOUS PAGE, FILL IN THE BLANKS BELOW TO FINISH THE SENTENCE.

"WHEN THE _COUNSELOR_ COMES, _WHOM_ I WILL _SEND_ TO _YOU_ FROM THE _FATHER_ , THE _SPIRIT_ OF _TRUTH_ WHO _GOES_ OUT FROM THE FATHER, HE WILL _TESTIFY_ _ABOUT_ ME."

JOHN 15:26

32

FIND THE WORDS BELOW IN THE WORDSEARCH PUZZLE.

```
H N P B T V W W V D L C D
O V Q V Q Y A B T R O A G S
H I W S N B T S K E J E T
N C H M I B H N S R L N R
F R O A S D O S E A T B Q T
N C Z L V T R U T H U I G J
A G O Q N D A E D K V U F F
B F I B W S G O O U R K T V
O I E M J B E B L E B D G R
H N P B T V W V J D L C D
O V Q V Q Y A R P A O H A G R S
H I W S L E S P I R I T L T
N T H S N I B H X K R Y O U
```

SPIRIT   WHOM   YOU

ABOUT   TRUTH   TESTIFY

GOES   COUNSELOR   SEND

33

COLOR THE PICTURE

WHEN YOU BECOME A CHILD OF WHERE DOES THE HOLY SPIRIT L

GO ON TO THE NEXT PAGE TO FI THE ANSWER.

34

USE THE CODE CHART BELOW TO MATCH THE CODES WITH LETTERS. USE THE COLUMN GOING DOWN, FIRST, THEN WRITE THE LETTERS IN THE BLANKS.

	1	2	3	4	5	6	7
1	A	H	I	P	Q	X	Y
2	B	G	J	O	R	W	Z
3	C	F	K	N	S	V	!
4	D	E	L	M	T	U	

DO YOU NOT KNOW
THAT YOUR BODY
IS A TEMPLE OF
THE HOLY SPIRIT
WHO IS IN YOU,
WHOM YOU HAVE
RECEIVED FROM GOD"

1 Corinthians 6:19

35

THE HOLY SPIRIT ACTUALLY COMES TO LIVE INSIDE YOU ! YOUR BODY BECOMES THE TEMPLE, OR DWELLING PLACE, OF GOD'S SPIRIT.

THIS IS HARD TO UNDERSTAND BECAUSE WE CAN'T SEE HIM, BUT IT'S TRUE BECAUSE THE BIBLE SAYS IT'S SO. MANY TIMES THE HOLY SPIRIT MAKES HIS PRESENCE KNOWN. WE CAN FEEL HIM AS HE GIVES US HIS POWER AND STRENGTH TO LIVE AS GOD WANTS US TO LIVE.

CONNECT-THE-DOTS

36

ONCE, OUR HUMAN SPIRITS WERE DEAD. WE WERE BORN SPIRITUALLY DEAD. JESUS GIVES US NEW LIFE IN OUR SPIRITS !

" FOR JUST AS THE FATHER RAISES THE DEAD AND GIVES THEM LIFE, EVEN SO THE SON GIVES LIFE TO WHOM HE IS PLEASED TO GIVE IT. "

John 5:21

GO TO THE NEXT PAGE. USING THE GRID, DRAW THE ABOVE PICTURE FOR YOURSELF.

37

FROM THE PREVIOUS PAGE, USE THE GRID TO DRAW THE PICTURE FOR YOURSELF.

38

NOW THAT YOU ARE A CHRISTIAN, YOU MUST LET THE HOLY SPIRIT TEACH YOU HOW TO LIVE YOUR NEW LIFE. HOW DOES HE DO THIS ?

USE THE CODE CHART BELOW TO MATCH THE CODES WITH LETTERS. USE THE COLUMN GOING DOWN, FIRST, THEN WRITE THE LETTERS IN THE BLANKS ON THE FOLLOWING PAGE.

	1	2	3	4	5	6	7
1	A	B	C	D	E	F	G
2	H	I	J	K	L	M	N
3	O	P	Q	R	S	T	U
4	V	W	X	Y	Z		

WHAT YOU PUT INTO YOUR MIND, WHAT YOU READ OR WATCH OR LISTEN TO, IS WHAT WILL COME OUT OF YOU. IF YOU PUT GOD'S WORD IN, IF YOU READ THE BIBLE REGULARLY, GOD'S CHARACTER WILL COME OUT OF YOU IN THE WAYS YOU THINK, ACT AND THE CHOICES YOU MAKE.

39

USING THE CODE CHART FROM THE PREVIOUS PAGE, COMPLETE THE VERSE BELOW.

"DO NOT CONFORM
ANY LONGER TO THE
PATTERN OF THIS
WORLD, BUT BE
TRANSFORMED BY
THE RENEWING
OF YOUR MIND"

Romans 12:2

40

COLOR THE PICTURE

BE CAREFUL IN YOUR CHOICES !

41

TRAVEL THE PATH THAT MAKES A SENTENCE.

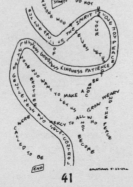

Galatians 5:22-23a

42

AFTER GOING THROUGH THE MAZE ON THE PREVIOUS PAGE, FILL IN THE BLANKS BELOW TO FINISH THE VERSE.

"BUT THE FRUIT OF
THE SPIRIT IS
LOVE, JOY,
PEACE,
PATIENCE,
KINDNESS,
GOODNESS,
FAITHFULNESS,
GENTLENESS
AND SELF-CONTROL"

Galatians 5:22-23 a

Page 43

FIND THE WORDS BELOW IN THE
WORDSEARCH PUZZLE.

```
C O S P I R I T A J B D 6
N A 2 D E T R U T H O I G O
A I T R A L O E D K V U F O
B T I W S F R U I T K T D
O W E N E B E C L E B D G N
U F P D T N U L O T D L C E
A U O N N A C E D N V U F S
B L I E W S G E D L T K T S
C N E S J B E L B B R R G R
H E W L B S P Y C C C O T
N S H S N I B H A R R O W
T S G E N T L E N E S S V V
H I W S L B P D I D T I L E
```

JOY   KINDNESS
SELF·CONTROL   SPIRIT
GENTLENESS   PATIENCE
PEACE   GOODNESS
FRUIT   LOVE
FAITHFULNESS

43

Page 44

THE FRUIT OF THE SPIRIT

FILL IN THE BLANKS.

PATIENCE

GOODNESS

LOVE

FAITHFULNESS

SELF-CONTROL   PEACE

KINDNESS   JOY

GENTLENESS

44

Page 45

YOU ALREADY KNOW THAT WHEN YOU
BECOME A CHRISTIAN, THE HOLY SPIRIT
COMES TO LIVE IN YOU. THE HOLY SPIRIT
WILL LEAD YOU INTO GOD'S TRUTH, AND
HE WILL DO THE WORK OF PRODUCING
GOD'S CHARACTER IN YOU. IF YOU WILL
LET HIM. YOU CAN DO THAT BY CHOOSING
TO DO WHAT GOD WANTS RATHER THAN
WHAT YOU WANT. THIS IS CALLED
SURRENDERING, OR GIVING UP, TO GOD'S
WILL.

GOD'S CHARACTER IS THE FRUIT OF
THE SPIRIT.

UNSCRAMBLE THE WORDS BELOW TO
FIND GOD'S CHARACTER, THE FRUIT OF
THE SPIRIT.

OVLE   L O V E
OYJ   J O Y
PCEEA   P E A C E
TIEENCPA   P A T I E N C E
DNNESKSI   K I N D N E S S
O6DOSSNE   G O O D N E S S
HTAIFLUNFSES
            F A I T H F U L N E S S
TNLEEEGSSN
            G E N T L E N E S S
- RTNSFLEOCLO
            S E L F - C O N T R O L

45

Page 46

FIND YOUR WAY THROUGH THE
OBSTACLES. THE THINGS OF THIS WORLD,
THAT WILL TRY TO PULL YOU AWAY FROM
WHAT GOD WOULD WANT YOU TO DO.

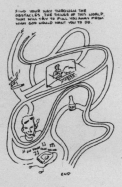

END

46

Page 47

FINISH THE PICTURE

AS YOU START TO LIVE YOUR NEW LIFE AS
GOD'S CHILD, IT IS IMPORTANT TO KNOW
WHO YOUR ENEMIES ARE!

THE CHRISTIAN HAS THREE ENEMIES:
1. THE DEVIL
2. THE SINFUL NATURE (THE FLESH)
3. THE WORLD

A CHRISTIAN IN THIS WORLD IS LIKE A
SOLDIER - A SOLDIER OF THE LORD.
YOUR ONLY WEAPON IS THE BIBLE

47

Page 48

USE THE CODE CHART BELOW TO MATCH
THE CODES WITH LETTERS. USE THE
COLUMN GOING DOWN, FIRST, THEN
WRITE THE LETTERS IN THE BLANKS.

	1	2	3	4	5	6	7
1	A	B	C	D	E	F	G
2	H	I	J	K	L	M	N
3	O	P	Q	R	S	T	U
4	V	W	X	Y	Z		

" BE SELF-CONTROLLED
AND ALERT. YOUR
ENEMY THE DEVIL
PROWLS AROUND
LIKE A ROARING
LION LOOKING
FOR SOMEONE
TO DEVOUR. "

1 PETER 5:8

48

Page 49

OUR LORD NEVER LEAVES HIS CHILDREN
HELPLESS. HE ALWAYS GIVES US A WAY
TO STAND AGAINST OUR ENEMY THE
DEVIL.
TO FIND OUT HOW, USE THE CODE CHART BELOW
TO COMPLETE THE VERSE. USE THE COLUMN
GOING DOWN FIRST.

	1	2	3	4	5	6	7
1	A	B	C	D	E	F	G
2	H	I	J	K	L	M	N
3	O	P	Q	R	S	T	U
4	V	W	X	Y	Z		

" SUBMIT YOUR-
SELVES THEN TO
GOD. RESIST
THE DEVIL
AND HE WILL
FLEE FROM YOU. "

JAMES 4:7

49

Page 50

CONNECT-THE-DOTS

"... RESIST THE DEVIL, AND HE WILL FLEE..."

50

Page 51

WHAT DO YOU NEED TO DO WHEN THE
DEVIL TEMPTS YOU TO SIN?

AS YOU GO THROUGH THE MAZE, COLLECT
THE LETTERS AND COMPLETE THE
STATEMENT BELOW.

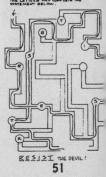

RESIST THE DEVIL!

51

WHAT IS THE DEVIL LIKE?

AS YOU GO THROUGH THIS MAZE, COLLECT THE LETTERS AND COMPLETE THE STATEMENT BELOW.

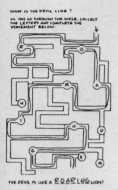

THE DEVIL IS LIKE A **R O A R I N G** LION!

52

PSALM 119 : 104 - 105 GIVES ANOTHER DESCRIPTION OF GOD'S WORD, THE BIBLE. USE THE CODE BELOW TO COMPLETE THESE TWO VERSES. USE THE COLUMN GOING DOWN FIRST.

	1	2	3	4	5	6	7
1	A	B	C	D	E	F	G
2	H	I	J	K	L	M	N
3	O	P	Q	R	S	T	U
4	V	W	X	Y	Z		

"I GAIN UNDER-
STANDING FROM
YOUR PRECEPTS:
THEREFORE I
HATE EVERY
WRONG PATH.
YOUR WORD IS A
LAMP TO MY FEET
AND A LIGHT FOR
MY PATH."

53

THE BIBLE IS A LAMP THAT LIGHTS OUR WAY IN THE DARKNESS OF SIN AND TEMPTATION.

USING THE GRID, DRAW THE PICTURE BELOW ON THE NEXT PAGE.

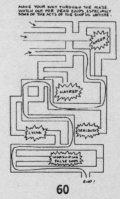

54

FROM THE PREVIOUS PAGE, USE THE GRID TO DRAW THE PICTURE FOR YOURSELF.

55

THE SECOND ENEMY IN OUR WALK WITH THE LORD IS OUR SINFUL NATURE, ALSO KNOWN AS THE "FLESH". THIS SINFUL NATURE OR FLESH IS A PART OF ALL OF US. WE ARE BORN WITH IT.

USE THE CODE CHART BELOW TO MATCH THE CODES WITH LETTERS. USE THE COLUMN GOING DOWN, FIRST, THEN WRITE THE LETTERS IN THE BLANKS.

	1	2	3	4	5	6	7
4		Z	Y	X	W	V	
3	O	P	Q	R	S	T	U
2	N	M	L	K	J	I	H
1	A	B	C	D	E	F	G

"THE ACTS OF THE
SINFUL NATURE ARE
ANGER, JEALOUSY,
NOT SHARING, HATING,
LYING, MAKING OTHERS
ANGRY, WORSHIPING
FALSE GODS, AND
WITCHCRAFT."
GALATIANS 5:19-21
(PARAPHRASED BIBLE)

56

FIND THE WORDS BELOW IN THE WORDSEARCH PUZZLE.

WORSHIPING   ANGRY
ACTS   JEALOUSY
SINFUL   HATING
NATURE   LYING
FLESH   SHARING

57

THE BIBLE TELLS US HOW TO FIGHT THE DESIRES OF THE SINFUL NATURE.

USE THE CODE CHART BELOW TO MATCH THE CODES WITH LETTERS. USE THE COLUMN GOING DOWN, FIRST, THEN WRITE THE LETTERS IN THE BLANKS.

	1	2	3	4	5	6	7
4		Z	Y	X	W	V	
3	O	P	Q	R	S	T	U
2	N	M	L	K	J	I	H
1	A	B	C	D	E	F	G

"THOSE WHO BELONG TO
CHRIST JESUS HAVE
CRUCIFIED THE SINFUL
NATURE WITH ITS
PASSIONS AND DESIRES.
SINCE WE LIVE BY THE
SPIRIT, LET US KEEP
IN STEP WITH THE
SPIRIT."
GALATIANS 5:24-25

58

FIND THE WORDS BELOW IN THE WORDSEARCH PUZZLE.

JESUS   STEP
SPIRIT   DESIRES
BELONG   KEEP
PASSIONS   CHRIST
CRUCIFIED   LIVE

59

MAKE YOUR WAY THROUGH THE MAZE. WATCH OUT FOR DEAD ENDS, ESPECIALLY SOME OF THE ACTS OF THE SINFUL NATURE.

ANGER
HATRED
LYING
JEALOUSY
WORSHIPING FALSE GODS

END!

60

SUGGESTED
FINISH THE FACE
YOU DO THE DRAWING! DRAW THE
EXPRESSION FOR JOY:

JOY— A FRUIT OF THE HOLY SPIRIT!

61

SUGGESTED
FINISH THE FACE
YOU DO THE DRAWING! DRAW THE
EXPRESSION FOR PEACE:

PEACE — A FRUIT OF THE HOLY SPIRIT!

62

SUGGESTED
FINISH THE FACE
YOU DO THE DRAWING! DRAW THE
EXPRESSION FOR LOVE:

LOVE — A FRUIT OF THE HOLY SPIRIT!

63

SUGGESTED
FINISH THE FACE
YOU DO THE DRAWING! DRAW THE
EXPRESSION FOR ANGER:

ANGER — AN ACT OF THE SINFUL NATURE.

64

SUGGESTED
FINISH THE FACE
YOU DO THE DRAWING! DRAW THE
EXPRESSION FOR HATRED!

HATRED — AN ACT OF THE SINFUL NATURE

65

THE THIRD ENEMY IN OUR LIVES WITH GOD
IS THE WORLD.

IT IS NOT THE WORLD IN ITSELF THAT IS
OUR ENEMY AS GOD CREATED THE WORLD.
IT IS SOME OF THE THINGS IN THE WORLD
THAT CAN LEAD US AWAY FROM GOD AND
WHAT HE WANTS US TO DO.

GO THROUGH THE MAZE.

66

CIRCLE THESE THINGS THAT COULD BE USED
TO TEMPT YOU TO SIN AND TAKE YOU AWAY
FROM GOD'S PLAN FOR YOUR LIFE
(YOU MAY BE SURPRISED!)

A LOT OF THINGS CAN
BE USED FOR BAD AS WELL
AS GOOD!

67

WHAT DOES GOD SAY ABOUT THE THINGS OF
THE WORLD?

USE THE CODE CHART BELOW TO MATCH
THE CODES WITH LETTERS. USE THE
COLUMN GOING DOWN, FIRST, THEN WRITE
THE LETTERS IN THE BLANKS.

	1	2	3	4	5	6	7
4			Z	Y	X	W	V
3	O	P	Q	R	S	T	U
2	N	M	L	K	J	I	H
1	A	B	C	D	E	F	G

"DO NOT LOVE THE
WORLD OR ANYTHING
IN THE WORLD. IF
ANYONE LOVES THE
WORLD, THE LOVE OF
THE FATHER IS NOT
IN HIM"

1 JOHN 2:15

68

UNSCRAMBLE THE UNDERLINED WORDS
AND PLACE THEM IN THE CORRECT SPACE
IN THE CROSSWORD GRID ON THE NEXT PAGE.

ACROSS

1. THE HOLY SPIRIT WILL LEAD YOU INTO
ALL _T U H T_ .

2. YOUR _Y B D O_ IS THE TEMPLE OF THE
HOLY SPIRIT.

3. YOU HAVE THREE ENEMIES. ONE OF THEM
IS THE _IVDEL_ .

4. ANOTHER OF YOUR ENEMIES IS YOUR
FLESH, OR THE SINFUL _AERTUN_ .

DOWN

5. THE HOLY SPIRIT IS ALSO CALLED
THE _LORSECNOUL_ .

6. YOU ARE TO BE CHANGED BY THE
RENEWING OF YOUR _NMDI_ .

7. THE HOLY SPIRIT WILL PRODUCE
GOD'S _TFIUR_ IN YOU.

8. YOUR THIRD ENEMY IS THE THINGS
OF THE _RWLDO_ .

WORD LIST

MIND	DEVIL
BODY	NATURE
COUNSELOR	TRUTH
WORLD	FRUIT

69

70

EVEN THOUGH YOU ARE NOW GOD'S CHILD, YOU WILL STILL SIN. WHAT DO YOU DO THEN? TRAVEL THE PATH THAT MAKES A SENTENCE.

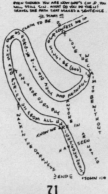

71

AFTER GOING THROUGH THE MAZE ON THE PREVIOUS PAGE, FILL IN THE BLANKS BELOW TO FINISH THE VERSE.

"IF WE CONFESS OUR SINS, HE (GOD) IS FAITHFUL AND JUST AND WILL FORGIVE US OUR SINS AND PURIFY US FROM ALL UNRIGHTEOUSNESS."

1 JOHN 1:9

72

FIND THE WORDS BELOW IN THE WORDSEARCH PUZZLE.

FORGIVE   SINS

FAITHFUL   JUST

PURIFY   CONFESS

UNRIGHTEOUSNESS

73

OUR LORD JESUS PAID THE PRICE FOR OUR SINS. HE TOOK OUR PUNISHMENT BY DYING ON THE CROSS.

USING THE GRID, DRAW THE PICTURE BELOW ON THE NEXT PAGE

74

FROM THE PREVIOUS PAGE, USE THE GRID TO DRAW THE PICTURE FOR YOURSELF.

75

ALL CHRISTIANS ARE TEMPTED TO SIN, TO DO THINGS THAT ARE WRONG. BUT WE CAN TRUST GOD TO HELP US IN OUR TIMES OF TEMPTATION.

USE THE CODE CHART BELOW TO MATCH THE CODES WITH LETTERS. USE THE COLUMN GOING DOWN, FIRST, THEN WRITE THE LETTERS IN THE BLANKS.

	7	6	5	4	3	2	1
1	A	H	I	P	Q	X	Y
2	B	G	J	O	R	W	Z
3	C	F	K	N	S	V	
4	D	E	L	M	T	U	

"THE ONLY TEMPTATIONS THAT YOU HAVE ARE THE TEMPTATIONS THAT ALL PEOPLE

CONT'D NEXT PAGE ...

76

CONT'D FROM PREVIOUS PAGE

HAVE. BUT YOU CAN TRUST GOD. HE WILL NOT LET YOU BE TEMPTED MORE THAN YOU CAN STAND. BUT WHEN YOU ARE, GOD WILL ALSO GIVE YOU A WAY TO ESCAPE THAT TEMPTATION. THEN YOU WILL BE ABLE TO STAND IT."

1 CORINTHIANS 10:13
(CHILDREN'S BIBLE)

77

CONNECT-THE-DOTS

FIGHTING TEMPTATION ON YOUR OWN.

78

CONNECT-THE-DOTS

FIGHTING TEMPTATION WITH GOD!

79

SOMETIMES YOU MAY NOT FEEL LIKE YOU ARE A CHRISTIAN. YOU MAY EVEN WONDER IF JESUS REALLY DID COME INTO YOUR HEART.

USUALLY YOU FEEL LIKE THIS WHEN YOU KEEP MAKING THE SAME MISTAKE OVER AND OVER, OR WHEN IT SEEMS LIKE YOU ARE ALWAYS TEMPTED TO DO WHAT YOU KNOW IS SIN.

JESUS NEVER LIES; THE BIBLE IS TRUE. IF YOU REALLY MEANT IT WHEN YOU ASKED JESUS INTO YOUR HEART, THEN YOU CAN BELIEVE THAT JESUS IS IN YOU.

THIS IS WHAT GOD'S WORD SAYS:

80

THE ONLY WAY TO HEAVEN IS THROUGH JESUS CHRIST. HAVING JESUS IN YOUR HEART MEANS YOU HAVE BEEN GIVEN ETERNAL LIFE, AND YOU WILL LIVE WITH GOD FOREVER. THIS IS GOD'S PROMISE TO YOU!

FIND THE UNDERLINED WORDS IN THE WORDSEARCH PUZZLE BELOW

"I GIVE THEM ETERNAL LIFE, AND THEY SHALL NEVER PERISH; NO ONE CAN SNATCH THEM OUT OF MY HAND."

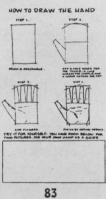

81

FROM THE START OF YOUR CHRISTIAN LIFE TO THE END OF IT, YOU WILL ALWAYS STAY IN THE HAND OF THE LORD JESUS.

LIFE WILL NOT ALWAYS BE EASY, BUT JESUS WILL GET YOU THROUGH!

FIND YOUR WAY THROUGH THE MAZE OF LIFE.

82

HOW TO DRAW THE HAND

TRY IT FOR YOURSELF. YOU HAVE ROOM BELOW FOR TWO PICTURES. USE YOUR OWN HAND AS A GUIDE

83

UNSCRAMBLE THE UNDERLINED WORDS AND PLACE THEM IN THE CROSSWORD GRID ON THE NEXT PAGE.

ACROSS

1. WE ARE TO SSFCNOE OUR SINS TO GOD.

2. WE ARE ALL PTMTEDE TO SIN.

3. THE BIBLE SAYS THAT PEOPLE ARE LIKE PHESE.

4. NO ONE CAN AESTL US OUT OF GOD'S HAND.

DOWN

1. GOD WILL MAKE OUR HEARTS CLNAE AND NEW.

2. GOD WILL EFGRVO! US FOR OUR SINS.

3. THE TEMPTATIONS THAT COME ARE WHAT COME TO ALL EEPOLP.

4. GOD WILL GIVE US A WAY TO ESCAPE TEMPTATION SO WE CAN ASDNT.

WORD LIST

SHEEP	PEOPLE
STAND	FORGIVE
CONFESS	STEAL
TEMPTED	CLEAN

84

85

IF YOU REMEMBER, WHEN YOU INVITE JESUS CHRIST INTO YOUR LIFE, YOUR BODY BECOMES THE TEMPLE OF GOD'S HOLY SPIRIT

IN OTHER WORDS, YOUR BODY BECOMES THE "HOUSE" THAT THE HOLY SPIRIT DWELLS IN. AS YOU LIVE IN A HOUSE THAT NEEDS CLEANING, SO DOES YOUR "BODY-HOUSE" NEED CLEANING. THE HOLY SPIRIT WANTS TO CLEAN UP WRONG THINKING AND ACTIONS.

THE HOUSE WITHOUT JESUS:

COLOR THE PICTURE.

86

NOW THAT THE HOLY SPIRIT LIVES IN YOU, HE IS GOING TO WANT TO CLEAN AND EVEN CHANGE SOME THINGS IN HIS HOUSE!

THIS TAKES TIME BUT THE RESULT IS THAT YOU ARE MADE FREE AND MUCH HAPPIER. AND JUST LIKE A NICE CLEAN HOUSE, YOU ARE MORE INVITING TO OTHERS. PEOPLE WILL WANT TO BE AROUND YOU, AND YOU CAN SHARE WITH THEM WHAT JESUS HAS DONE IN YOUR LIFE!

THE HOUSE WITH JESUS:

COLOR THE PICTURE.

87

88

GO THROUGH THE HOUSE BELOW AND PICK UP THOSE THINGS THAT GOD WOULD CLEAN OUT. WRITE THEM IN THE BLANK SPACES BELOW.

HATRED
KINDNESS
PEACE
STEALING
JOY
PATIENCE
LOVE
LAZINESS
DISOBEDIENCE
CHEATING
LYING
ANGER
SELF-CONTROL
FEAR
GOODNESS
GENTLENESS

FEAR	STEALING
ANGER	HATRED
LYING	LAZINESS
DISOBEDIENCE	CHEATING

88

89

AGAIN, IT IS THE WORK OF THE HOLY SPIRIT IN US. HE ONLY NEEDS US TO BE WILLING TO LET HIM DO THAT WORK.

GOD'S WORD GIVES US A PROMISE!

FIND THE UNDERLINED WORDS IN THE WORDSEARCH PUZZLE BELOW.

"BE CONFIDENT OF THIS, THAT HE WHO BEGAN A GOOD WORK IN YOU WILL CARRY IT ON TO THE FINISH UNTIL JESUS CHRIST COMES AGAIN."

PHILIPPIANS 1:6
(CHILDREN'S BIBLE)

```
P Q G T N F B V N D C V D
T S W S C U L E E W S R U T
N O R K H E R B V R N A C
F A E H I W S L B X X I N G
I L E F U E G L C A J N H
M Q G T G F T V N N A W C R
I U L C O N F I D E N T P
S L N H O B B L S B G H F S
H P E R O S H J E S U S W T
E L N E B J B X V B Z T L D
```

89

90

PICTURE YOURSELF AS A SOLDIER! YOU ARE NOW A SOLDIER FOR JESUS CHRIST, AND HE GIVES US EVERYTHING WE NEED TO WIN THE BATTLE.

USE THE CODE CHART BELOW TO MATCH THE CODES WITH LETTERS. USE THE COLUMN GOING DOWN FIRST, THEN WRITE THE LETTERS IN THE BLANKS.

	1	2	3	4	5	6
5	A	F	K	P	U	Z
4	B	G	L	Q	V	
3	C	H	M	R	W	
2	D	I	N	S	X	
1	E	J	O	T	Y	

F I N A L L Y , B E
S T R O N G I N T H E
L O R D A N D I N H I S
M I G H T Y P O W E R .

CONT'D NEXT PAGE...

90

91

CONT'D FROM PREVIOUS PAGE.

P U T O N T H E F U L L
A R M O R O F G O D
S O T H A T Y O U C A N
T A K E Y O U R S T A N D
A G A I N S T T H E
D E V I L ' S S C H E M E S "

EPHESIANS 6:10-11

91

92

FIND THE UNDERLINED WORDS IN THE WORDSEARCH PUZZLE BELOW.

"STAND FIRM THEN, WITH THE BELT OF TRUTH BUCKLED AROUND YOUR WAIST, WITH THE BREASTPLATE OF RIGHTEOUSNESS IN PLACE, AND WITH YOUR FEET FITTED WITH THE READINESS THAT COMES FROM THE GOSPEL OF PEACE. IN ADDITION TO ALL THIS, TAKE UP THE SHIELD OF FAITH, WITH WHICH YOU CAN EXTINGUISH ALL THE FLAMING ARROWS OF THE EVIL ONE. TAKE THE HELMET OF SALVATION AND THE SWORD OF THE SPIRIT, WHICH IS THE WORD OF GOD."

EPHESIANS 6:14-17

THIS IS THE FULL ARMOR OF GOD!

```
I U L C H N F G O S P E L
S L B R E A S T P L A T E D
H P E R L S A H S U W N
E L N E M J B I R L L L D
M Q G T E E B V N E X C V T
O S F I T T E D O A L P H R
R W B R K H E R G L R D A U
O A E H I W S L B D P T W T
I L S A L V A T I O N N H
S W O R D F T V N N A W C R
```

SHIELD   FITTED
WORD   TRUTH
HELMET   SWORD
BELT   GOSPEL
SALVATION   BREASTPLATE

92

93

FILL IN THE BLANKS.

SWORD OF THE
SPIRIT

HELMET OF
SALVATION

SHOES OF
THE GOSPEL

BELT OF TRUTH

BREASTPLATE
OF
RIGHTEOUSNESS

SHIELD OF
FAITH

THE FULL ARMOR OF GOD!

93

94

FINISH THE PICTURE.

DRAW OVER THE DOTTED LINES TO "DRESS" IN THE ARMOR OF GOD.

94

95

FIND YOUR WAY THROUGH THE BATTLEFIELD OF LIFE. WATCH OUT FOR TEMPTATION AND SIN!

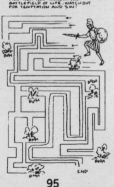

END

95

96

DO YOU REMEMBER OUR THREE ENEMIES, THE WORLD, THE FLESH (OR SINFUL NATURE), AND THE DEVIL?

WE CALL THE BATTLE AGAINST THESE ENEMIES SPIRITUAL WARFARE!

GOD'S WORD HAS SOMETHING TO SAY ABOUT THIS WARFARE.

"FOR OUR STRUGGLE (OUR BATTLE) IS NOT AGAINST FLESH AND BLOOD, BUT AGAINST THE RULERS, AGAINST THE AUTHORITIES, AGAINST THE POWERS OF THIS DARK WORLD AND AGAINST THE SPIRITUAL FORCES OF EVIL IN THE HEAVENLY REALMS (THE UNSEEN SPIRITUAL WORLD AROUND US)."
EPHESIANS 6:12

96

FIND THE WORDS BELOW IN THE WORD SEARCH.

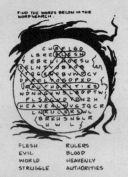

FLESH
EVIL
WORLD
STRUGGLE

RULERS
BLOOD
HEAVENLY
AUTHORITIES

97

NOW IT IS TIME TO START LIVING YOUR LIFE AS A CHILD OF GOD.

THERE ARE MANY THINGS IN LIFE THAT CAN DISTRACT US, OR LEAD US AWAY, FROM JESUS.

WHAT DOES JESUS SAY WE SHOULD DO?

UNSCRAMBLE THE WORDS AND PUT THEM IN THE RIGHT PLACES IN THE VERSE BELOW

" LET US XFI OUR EYES ON JESUS, THE RATUHO AND PERFECTER OF OUR AEFIT, WHO FOR THE OYJ SET EBRFEO HIM ENDURED THE OCSCS, SCORNING ITS MHSEA, AND SAT NODW AT THE RIGHT NPHA OF THE HTNROE OF GOD."

HEBREWS 12:2

" LET US FIX OUR EYES ON JESUS, THE AUTHOR AND PERFECTER OF OUR FAITH, WHO FOR THE JOY SET BEFORE HIM ENDURED THE CROSS, SCORNING ITS SHAME, AND SAT DOWN AT THE RIGHT HAND OF THE THRONE OF GOD."

98

ANSWERS

99

103

100

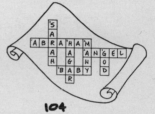

104

101

105

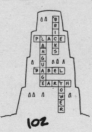

102

106

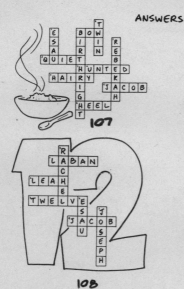

107

T
ESAU BOWIN
BIRTH TWIN
REB
QUIET
HUNTED
HAIRY
JACOB
HEEL

108

R
LABAN
RACHE
LEAH
TWELVE
ESAU J
JACOB O
SEPH

109

B B
LOVED
COAT JACOB
COLORS
TWO
TEN
BENJAMIN

110

H
BUTLER
BAKER A
EGYPT
H
DREAMS
R
PRISON
WITH

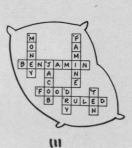

111

MONY F
FAMINE
BENJAMIN
JACOB
FOOD RULED
N

112

U R
PRINCESS
BASKET MOTHER
SISTER
SON

113

B
BLOOD
LICE
FLIES FROGS
FIR
H
DARKNESS
LOCUSTS

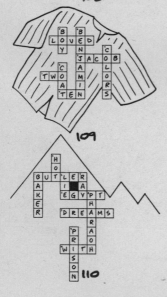

114

I
MOSES
AARON
LEFT
CLOUD
EGYPT
HERDS

ANSWERS

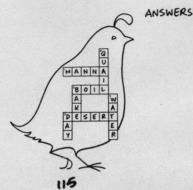

115
Crossword: QUAIL, MANNA, BOIL, BAKE, WATER, DESERT, KAY

119
Crossword: HIT, WALL, GO, ANGEL, DONKEY, SWORD

116
Crossword: MOUNT, TOP, SINAI, AFRAID, IDO, THUNDER

120
Crossword: PRIESTS, ARK, TWELVE, WATER, DRY, STONES

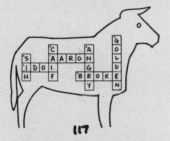

117
Crossword: SIN, IDOL, AARON, ANGRY, GOLDEN, BROKE

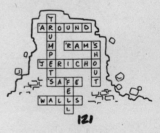

121
Crossword: TRUMPET, AROUND, RAMS, SHOUT, JERICHO, SAFE, WALLS

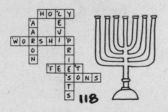

118
Crossword: HOLY, SEVEN, AARON, WORSHIP, PRIESTS, FEET, SONS

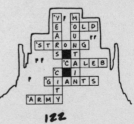

122
Crossword: YEAR, MOLD, HOUSE, STRONG, IT, CALEB, CITY, GIANTS, ARMY

ANSWERS

123

124

125

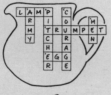

126

127

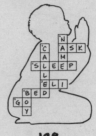

128

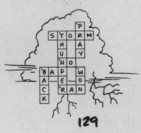

129

130

ANSWERS

131

135

132

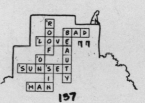

136

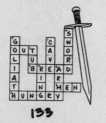

133

137

134

138

139

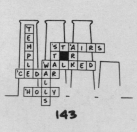

143

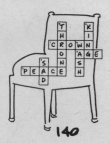

140

144

141

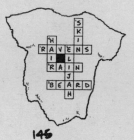

145

142

146

ANSWERS

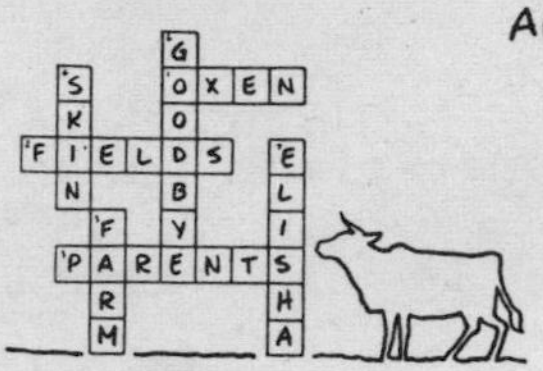
SKIN
OXEN
GOOD BOY
FIELDS
ELISHA
FARM
PARENTS

147

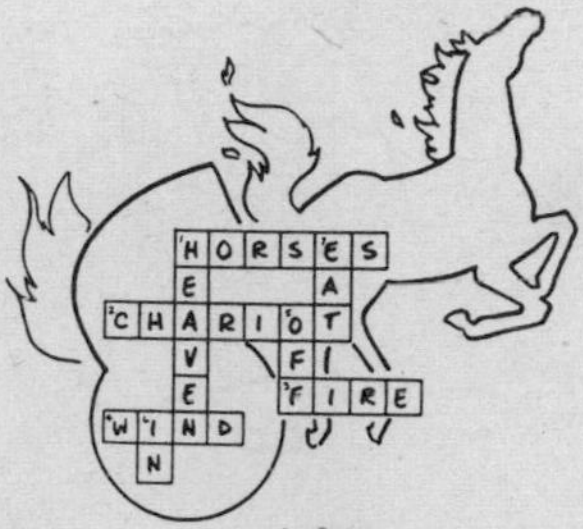
HORSES
CHARIOT
OFF
FIRE
WIND

148

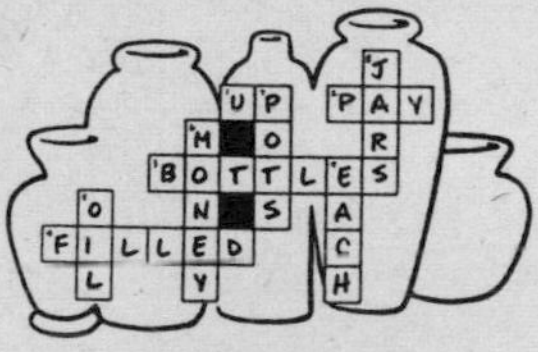
UP
PAY
BOTTLES
FILLED
OIL
EACH

149

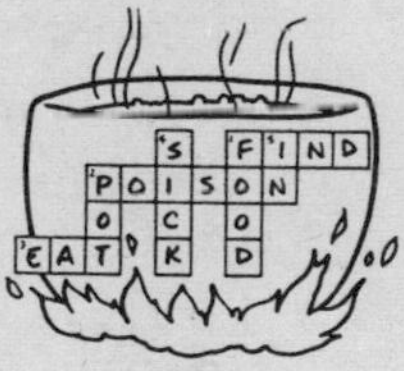
FIND
POISON
EAT
COOK
FOOD

150

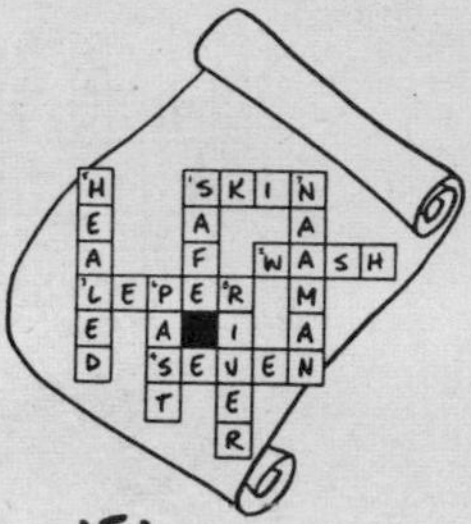
HEALED
SKIN
NAAMAN
WASH
LEPER
SEVEN
RIVER

151

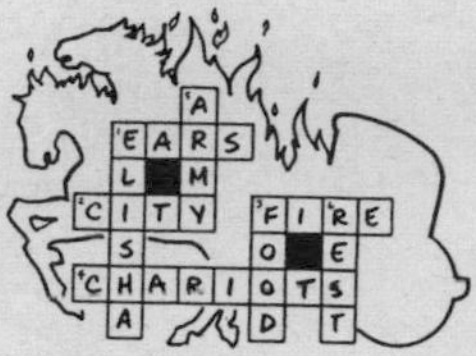
EARS
CITY
FIRE
CHARIOTS

152

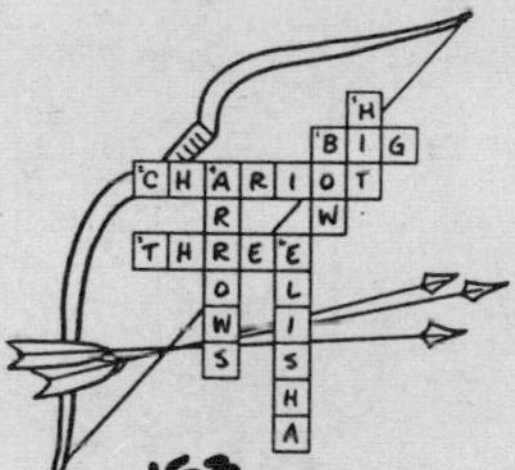
BIG
CHARIOT
BOW
ARROWS
THREE
ELISHA

153

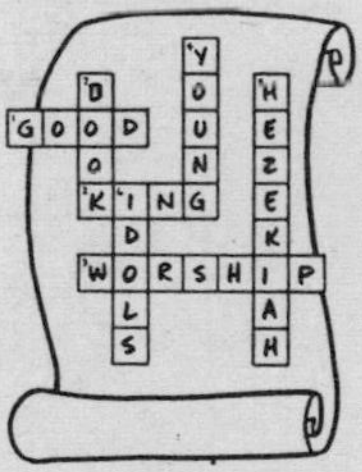
GOOD
YOUNG
HEZEKIAH
KING
WORSHIP
IDOLS

154

ANSWERS

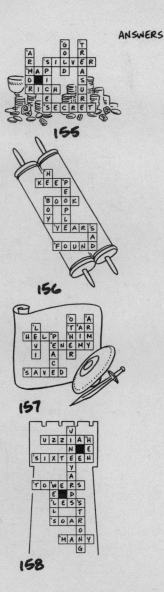

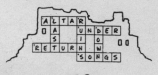

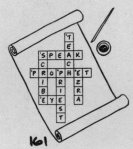

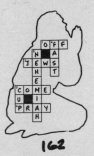

155

156

157

158

159

160

161

162

ANSWERS

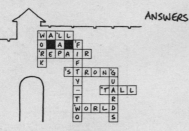

163

Crossword 163:
- WALL / L
- O / A / F
- REPAIR / F
- K / STRONG / G
- Y-T / TALL U
- WORLDS A
- O R D S

167

Crossword 167:
- EVIL
- V
- A
- SHEPHERD / L
- FOREVER / L
- P / E / E / Y
- STILL / GREEN / M
- LORD / DOW / E

164

Crossword 164:
- LON
- OVE / QGR
- BEAUTIFUL
- D / E / FL
- ESTHER
- CROWN S R

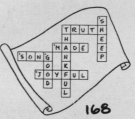

168

Crossword 168:
- SHEEP
- TRUTH
- H / E
- MADE
- SONG / N / P
- O / K
- JOYFUL
- L

165

Crossword 165:
- S
- MORDECAI / T
- A / A / R / T
- HONOR / HORSE
- E / OWN / L

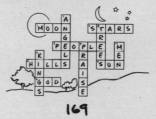

169

Crossword 169:
- A
- MOON / STARS
- PEOPLE / ME
- K / R / SUN
- HILLS / A
- N / G / I
- G / O / S
- D / E

166

Crossword 166:
- J
- LOVE / POOR
- M / A / B
- SUFFERING / O
- C / N / O
- HE / D
- GOD

170

Crossword 170:
- K
- TIME
- P / I
- HEAL / L
- TWO / CRY
- LOVE
- A
- BUILD
- G / I
- HATE **170**

ANSWERS

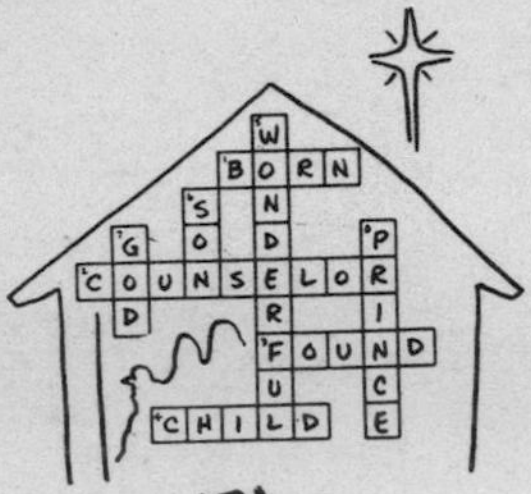
WONDERFUL
BORN
SON
GOD
COUNSELOR
PRINCE
FOUND
CHILD

171

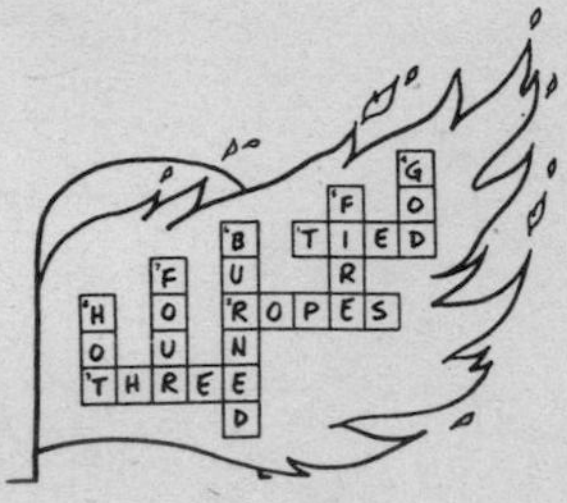
GO
FIRE
TIED
BURNED
FOUR
ROPES
HOT
THREE

175

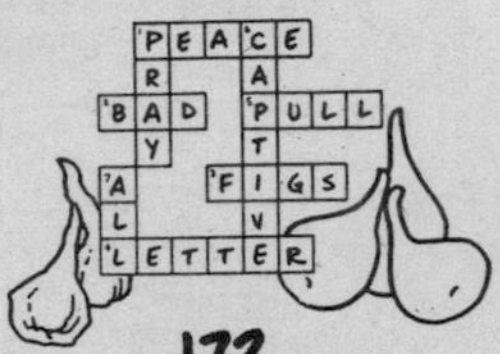
PEACE
CAPTIVE
BAD
PULL
FIGS
LETTER

172

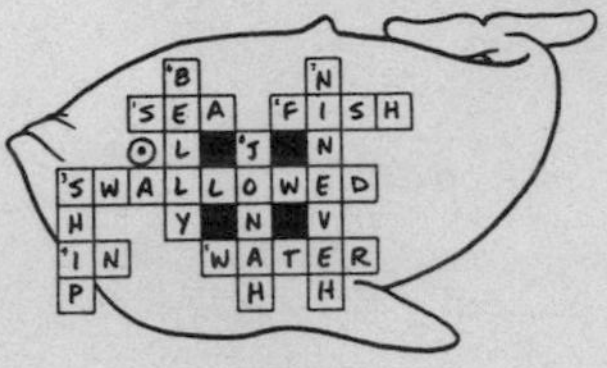
SEA
FISH
SWALLOWED
JONAH
IN
WATER

176

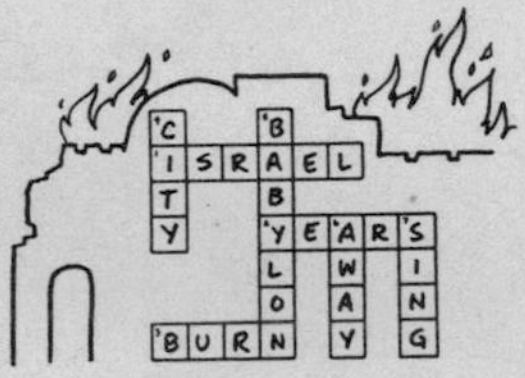
CITY
ISRAEL
BABYLON
YEARS
AWAY
SING
BURN

173

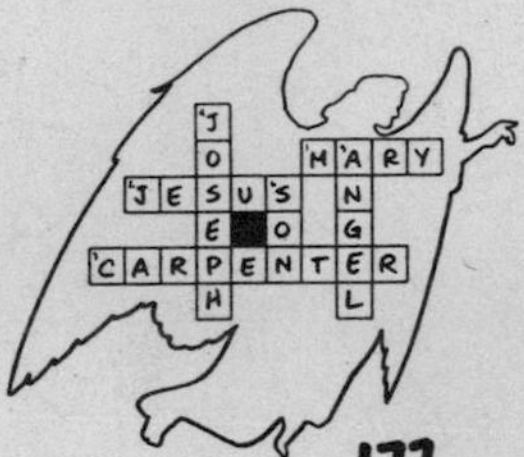
JOSEPH
MARY
JESUS
SON
ANGEL
CARPENTER

177

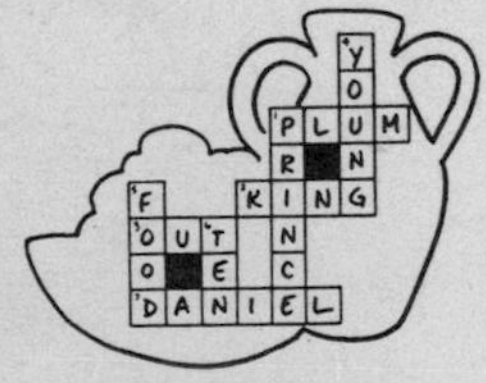
YOUNG
PLUM
KING
OUT
DANIEL

174

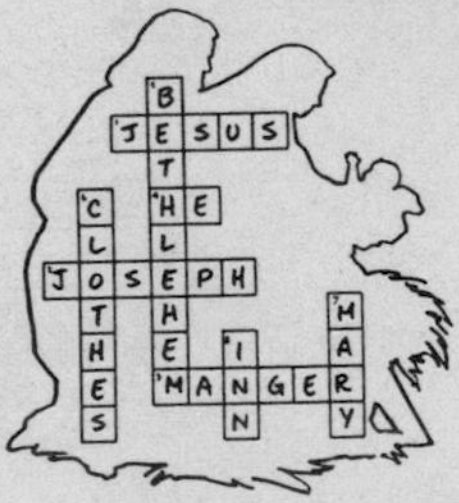
BETHLEHEM
JESUS
HE
CLOTHES
JOSEPH
MARY
MANGER

178

ANSWERS

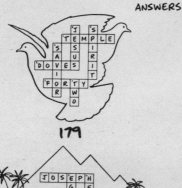

179

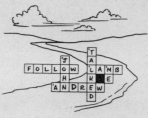

183

180

184

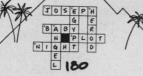

181

186

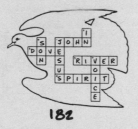

182

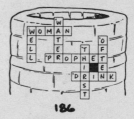

186

ANSWERS

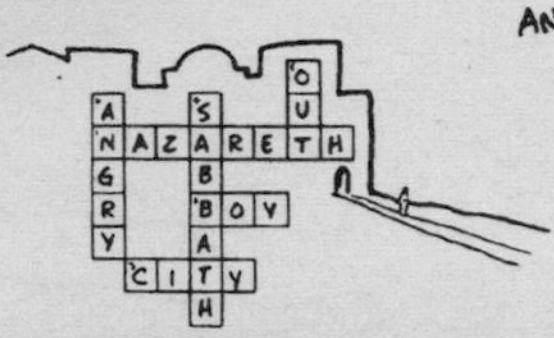
NAZARETH
BOY
CITY
ANGRY
SABBATH
OUT

187

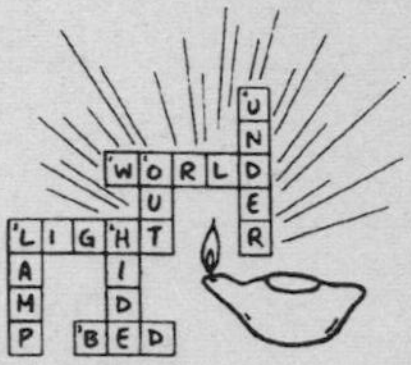
WORLD
LIGHT
BED
UNDER
OUT
HID
LAMP

192

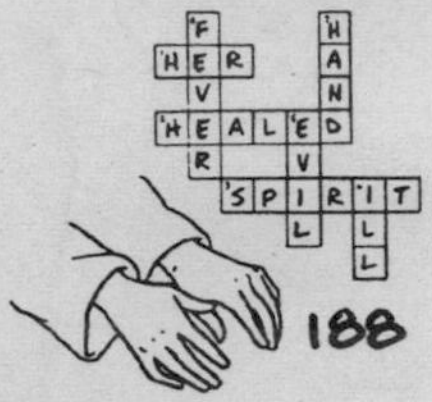
HER
HEALED
SPIRIT
FEVER
HAND
EVIL
ILL

188

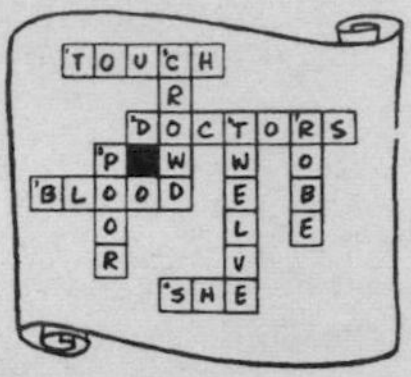
TOUCH
DOCTORS
BLOOD
SHE
CROWD
POOR
TWELVE
ROBE

193

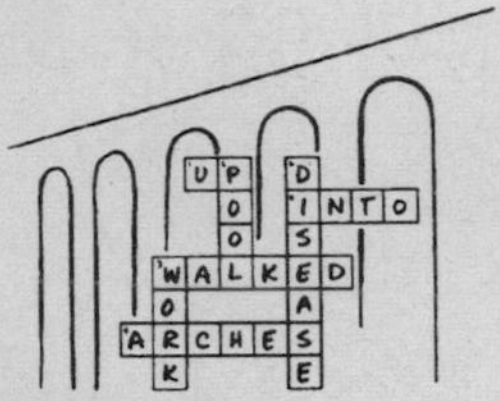
UP
INTO
WALKED
ARCHES
POOR
DISEASE
WORK

189

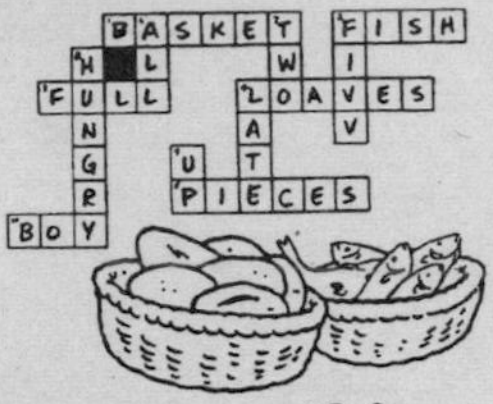
BASKET
FISH
FULL
LOAVES
PIECES
BOY
HUNGRY
ALL
TWO
FIVE
UP

194

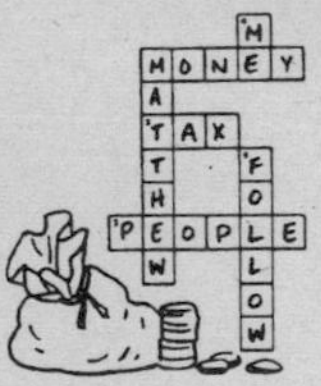
MONEY
TAX
PEOPLE
ME
MATTHEW
FOLLOW

190

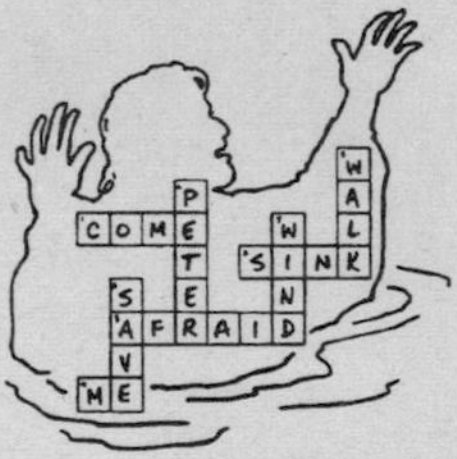
COME
SINK
AFRAID
ME
PETER
WALK
WIND
SAVE

195

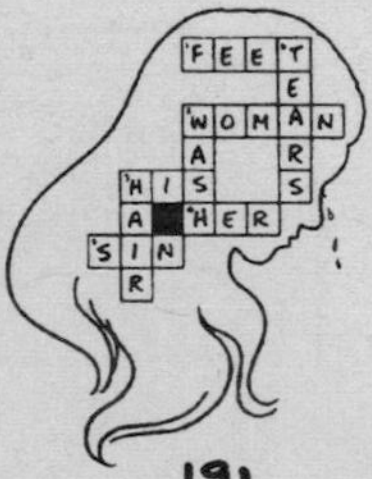
FEET
WOMAN
HIS
HER
SIN
TEARS
WASH
HAIR

191

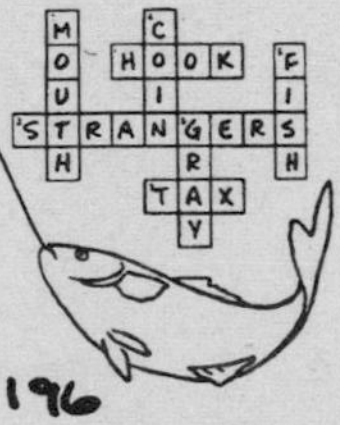
HOOK
STRANGERS
TAX
MOUTH
COIN
FISH

196